Cooperative Learning &
Pre-Algebra

Secondary Activities

by Becky Bride

Kagan

Kagan

Kagan Publishing
981 Calle Amanecer
San Clemente, CA 92673
1 (800) 933-2667
www.KaganOnline.com

ISBN: 978-1-933445-00-7

TABLE OF CONTENTS

Acknowledgments..III
Introduction...IV

Chapter 1
WHOLE NUMBERS

Lesson	Page
1. Number Sense	3
2. Expressions	47
3. Equations	64

Chapter 3
DECIMALS

Lesson	Page
1. Number Sense	126
2. Expressions	152
3. Equations and Inequalities	162

Chapter 2
INTEGERS

Lesson	Page
1. Number Sense	78
2. Expressions	102
3. Equations and Inequalities	115

Chapter 4
FRACTIONS

Lesson	Page
1. Number Sense	172
2. Expressions	197
3. Equations and Inequalities	209

TABLE OF CONTENTS CONT...

Chapter 5

RATIO, PROPORTION, AND PERCENT

Lesson	Page
1. Ratio and Proportion	222
2. Percents	233

Chapter 6

COORDINATE PLANES

Lesson	Page
1. Graphing	250

Chapter 7

DATA ANALYSIS AND PROBABILITY

Lesson	Page
1. Data Analysis	264
2. Statistical Graphs	272
3. Probability	290

Cooperative Learning and Pre-Algebra: Becky Bride
Kagan Publishing • 1 (800) 933-2667 • www.KaganOnline.com

ACKNOWLEDGMENTS

Many people have helped to make this book possible. Thank you to my family, who understood when I took time away from them to write and edit. Without my family's support and encouragement this book would not be a reality. Thank you to Zach Mori and Taz Naravne, my student assistants extraordinaire, who helped edit this book. Their attention to detail and their mathematical prowess were indispensable. Thank you to the Lord who gave me the gifts and talents to teach and write and gave me the imagination needed to create the activities.

To Spencer and Laurie Kagan, thank you for introducing me to the structural approach to cooperative learning, which is the foundation of this book. It has given me an opportunity to share with other teachers how the structural approach to cooperative learning can be successfully implemented in the mathematics curriculum. Thank you for giving me the opportunity to share with others what you have shared with me. Most of all, thank you for the tools to teach effectively. Because of these tools, I love teaching more today than when I first began my teaching career over 20 years ago. Rather than experiencing burnout, I am invigorated in my teaching and have the opportunity to pass all that I have learned to my daughter who will soon join the teaching ranks.

Many thanks to the staff at Kagan Publishing, who took a rough draft and made it look beautiful. The creative book layout was designed by Denise Alphabet. Kim Fields edited the text. The icons, layout, and technical illustration were the brainstorm of Kellee LaVars. The cover was illustrated by Erin Kant and colored by Alex Core. Thank you to Jennifer Evans for reviewing the book. Her suggestions for changes, corrections, and comments were very helpful during the editing phase. A special thank you to Miguel Kagan and Becky Herrington who were my consultants, mentors, and project managers. I appreciate your encouragement and support.

A very special thank you to all the teachers who will use this book so their students' experience will be rich and engaging and whose Pre-Algebra foundation will be solid.

INTRODUCTION

I have a dream that concepts taught at one level would be mastered enough to build on at the next level, making extensive review unnecessary. To achieve my dream, this book was designed and organized to reinforce algebra concepts in every chapter. The book begins with a chapter on whole numbers because students are the most fluent with that set of numbers. The main algebra concepts learned in a Pre-Algebra course are introduced in this chapter. Since students are so familiar with the set of whole numbers, they can focus on learning the algebra concepts without the difficulty of arithmetic. Order of operations, exponents, expressions, one, and two-step equations, working with formulas, and graphing are all introduced. In the integer chapter, the students learn how to add, subtract, multiply, and divide integers and then use those skills with order of operations, exponents, expressions, one, and two-step equations and inequalities, working with formulas, graphing, and solving inequalities. The inequalities are introduced in this chapter because of the necessity of flipping the inequality symbol when multiplying or dividing both sides by a negative number. These same concepts are threaded through the fraction and decimal chapters. The formula part of each chapter has students work with many geometric formulas for area, perimeter, and volume. The graphing aspect has students graph numbers on a real number line and plot points on the coordinate plane. A focus on the scale of the number line or axes is emphasized. Percents are included in the ratio and proportion chapter because solving percent problems can be done with proportions connecting the two concepts. Proportions are solved algebraically reinforcing the algebra skills. The coordinate plane chapter sets the foundation for coordinate graphing in higher level mathematics. The data analysis and probability chapter is included because circle graphs reinforce percents and probability is an application of fractions.

Cooperative learning has transformed my teaching and increased my students' achievement. In fact, it has taken me from a burned-out teacher to a teacher that looks forward to another day in the classroom. Rather than teaching for a 20- to 30-minute period of time, I teach for 5 to 10 minutes, then have the students work with the concept I just taught through a cooperative learning activity. Research has shown that most brains become overloaded with information after about 10 minutes. Once a brain is overloaded, it cannot take in more. The purpose of the cooperative learning activities is to allow students to work with the concept just taught so that they will have more room to assimilate another concept in the next segment of teaching. These cooperative learning activities have 25 percent to 100 percent of the students actively working with the concept, rather than just one student answering a question that I would ask. When students are actively engaged in the learning process, they retain more and achievement goes up. The students enjoy the class more when they have an opportunity to work cooperatively. Kagan Cooperative Learning has structured the student interaction to the point that there are no "hogs" (students that want to do it all) and there are no "logs" (students who are willing to let another do it all). It adds variety to the classroom, students bond with their teammates, and they are more successful in mathematics than they ever have been. It is a win-win situation for all.

Cooperative Learning and Pre-Algebra: Becky Bride
Kagan Publishing • 1 (800) 933-2667 • www.KaganOnline.com

INTRODUCTION CONTINUED

I believe in discovery learning as much as I believe in cooperative learning. This book includes some exploratory activities that have students discover concepts. When students discover concepts, they are more likely to remember them. Because the book *Cooperative Learning and Algebra* has an exploratory activity for just about every algebra concept along with vocabulary development, I did not duplicate those activities in this book unless it was necessary. Many chapters will mention that exploratory activities can be found in the *Cooperative Learning and Algebra* book.

Each chapter is divided into lessons, and each lesson is divided into activities. At the beginning of each chapter is a detailed list of each lesson and the activities it contains, along with a synopsis of the chapter. Each lesson begins with a synopsis. Most of the lessons end with a synthesis activity where students generate a graphic organizer or concept map of the concepts that they have learned. Each lesson has teacher notes and structure directions, and the black-lines or transparencies for each activity follows these teacher notes. The chapters, lessons, and activities are numbered sequentially. In the right-hand corner of each activity is a number. The first number designates the chapter, the second number designates the lesson, and the last number designates the activity. This system makes navigating the book a breeze. Answers are included for most activities on the transparencies, blacklines, or in the teacher notes.

This book was written for the teacher. My hope is that this book will transform the Pre-Algebra curriculum by introducing and having students work with algebraic concepts as they review whole numbers, fractions, and decimals and integers. This gives the students a different take on these concepts and hopefully gives them a new, fresh spin on the arithmetic that they have already learned. Enjoy!

WHOLE NUMBERS

This chapter works with whole numbers. The lesson on number sense begins the development of the subsets of the real numbers by defining the sets of natural and whole numbers. Comparing numbers, graphing numbers on a number line and a coordinate plane, and divisibility of numbers is also included. The difference between terms and factors is begun here at an arithmetic perspective. Order of operations, so crucial in higher level mathematics, is explored and practiced. The lesson on expressions has students work with the inequality symbols with variables, extends the concepts of factors and terms to variable expressions, and reinforces order of operations through evaluation of expressions. Using variables in real-world applications clarifies the purpose of using variables. The expression lesson ends with connections to geometry. The lesson on equations introduces students to one- and two-step equation solving techniques that will be used in the next three chapters. This lesson ends with geometric connections.

LESSON 1 — NUMBER SENSE

ACTIVITY 1: Can You Define Me?
ACTIVITY 2: Classify Me
ACTIVITY 3: How Many Ways Can You Graph Me?
ACTIVITY 4: Compare Me
ACTIVITY 5: Compare Me Again
ACTIVITY 6: Plot My Point
ACTIVITY 7: Am I Divisible?
ACTIVITY 8: Prime or Composite?
ACTIVITY 9: Exploring Terms and Factors
ACTIVITY 10: Factors or Terms?
ACTIVITY 11: Rewrite Me
ACTIVITY 12: Exploring Add/Subtract vs. Multiply/Divide
ACTIVITY 13: What Do I Do First?
ACTIVITY 14: Evaluate Me
ACTIVITY 15: Exploring Multiply/Divide vs. Exponents
ACTIVITY 16: What Do I Do First?—Take 2
ACTIVITY 17: Evaluate Me—Take 2
ACTIVITY 18: Evaluate Me—Take 3
ACTIVITY 19: Exploring the Role of Grouping Symbols
ACTIVITY 20: Processing All the Operations
ACTIVITY 21: Find My Match
ACTIVITY 22: Where Do the Operations Go?
ACTIVITY 23: What Did We Learn?

LESSON 2 — EXPRESSIONS

ACTIVITY 1: Read Me Two Ways
ACTIVITY 2: Give an Example
ACTIVITY 3: Where Do I Belong?
ACTIVITY 4: Graph My Inequality
ACTIVITY 5: Factors or Terms?
ACTIVITY 6: Rewrite Me
ACTIVITY 7: Evaluate Me
ACTIVITY 8: Evaluate Me Simultaneously
ACTIVITY 9: Write Me in Symbols
ACTIVITY 10: Simplify My Expression
ACTIVITY 11: Write an Expression for My Application
ACTIVITY 12: Applying Expressions in Geometry
ACTIVITY 13: What Did We Learn?

Cooperative Learning and Pre-Algebra: Becky Bride
Kagan Publishing • 1 (800) 933-2667 • www.KaganOnline.com

WHOLE NUMBERS

LESSON

3 **EQUATIONS**

ACTIVITY 1: Getting at the Concept
ACTIVITY 2: Is the Variable Alone?
ACTIVITY 3: Who is Attached?
ACTIVITY 4: Name the Connecting Operation
ACTIVITY 5: Name the Disconnecting Operation
ACTIVITY 6: Solve Me
ACTIVITY 7: Solve Again
ACTIVITY 8: Who is Connected and How?
ACTIVITY 9: Who Gets Disconnected First?
ACTIVITY 10: Solve Me—Take 2
ACTIVITY 11: Putting It All Together
ACTIVITY 12: Find My Mistakes
ACTIVITY 13: Applying Equations
ACTIVITY 14: What Did We Learn?

Cooperative Learning and Pre-Algebra: Becky Bride
Kagan Publishing • 1 (800) 933-2667 • www.KaganOnline.com

LESSON 1
NUMBER SENSE

This lesson begins with students defining the sets of whole and natural numbers. Each chapter will introduce students to a new subset of the real numbers, reinforcing the sets previously learned. Students will compare numbers using inequality symbols. The goal is for students to master the inequality symbols so that the symbols themselves will not be an issue as they compare other types of numbers in later chapters. The students will graph numbers on the real number line and the coordinate plane. This lays the foundation of graphing that will repeat with the other subsets of real numbers. The concept of terms and factors is explored at an arithmetic level, so there will be an easy transition to those same concepts with variables. Order of operations is explored, so the students can discover which operations take precedence. There are several activities to practice the order of operations that follow. Synthesizing the lesson with a graphic organizer concludes this lesson.

ACTIVITY

CAN YOU DEFINE ME?

Exploratory

Solo
1. Individually, each student completes the exploration.

Pair Consensus
2. For each problem on the investigation, each student shares with his/her partner, using RallyRobin, his/her re-sponse. They discuss the problems that they disagree on, trying to come to consensus on the correct response. They mark the problems they can't reach consensus on so

they can focus on them during the team phase. Encourage the students to add to their responses if their partner verbalizes an understanding they did not see.

Team Consensus
3. Each pair shares their responses, using RallyRobin, with the other pair in their team, augmenting their responses if necessary. When the teams are through sharing, each student should have a detailed, complete summary

▶ **Structure**
• Solo-Pair Consensus-Team Consensus

▶ **Materials**
• Blackline 1.1.1 per student
• 1 pencil per student

ACTIVITY

2 CLASSIFY ME

▶ **Structure**
• RallyCoach

▶ **Materials**
• Transparency 1.1.2
• 1 sheet of paper and pencil per pair of students

This activity has students identify the set(s) of numbers to which each problem belongs. Letting students know that the sets of natural and whole numbers are subsets of the real number system begins to develop the interrelationship among all of the sets of numbers. That is why real numbers are included in the directions.

Numeric

1. Teacher poses many problems using Transparency 1.1.2.

2. Partner A classifies the number in problem one as a natural, whole, and/or real number writing his/her response on the paper.

3. Partner B watches, listens, checks, and praises.

4. Partner B classifies the number in the next problem.

5. Partner A watches, listens, checks, and praises.

6. Repeat for remaining problems starting at step 2.

ACTIVITY

3 HOW MANY WAYS CAN YOU GRAPH ME?

▶ **Structure**
• RallyCoach

▶ **Materials**
• Transparency 1.1.3
• 1 sheet of paper, pencil, and ruler per pair of students

The purpose of this activity is to have students graph the same inequality using different scales. One of the difficulties in graphing, especially real-world data, is setting the scale on the number line or axes if the graph is in the coordinate plane. This activity will also appear in the integer, decimal, and fraction chapters, so students can work with different scales with those types of numbers.

Graphic

1. Teacher poses many problems using Transparency 1.1.3.

2. Partner A graphs the number in the first problem on a number line, using any scale he/she chooses.

3. Partner B watches, listens, checks, and praises.

4. Partner B graphs the number on a different number line using a different scale of his/her choice.

5. Partner A watches, listens, checks, and praises.

6. Repeat until five graphs are graphed for problem one.

7. Repeat for remaining problems starting at step 2.

Cooperative Learning and Pre-Algebra: Becky Bride
Kagan Publishing • 1 (800) 933-2667 • www.KaganOnline.com

ACTIVITY
4 COMPARE ME

Numeric

This activity may seem elementary for the students. The purpose of this activity is to ensure that the students can correctly place inequality symbols between two whole numbers. This activity also asks the students to write two sentences—one reading the expression from left to right, then the other one reading the expression from right to left. This will lay the groundwork for when students need to graph an inequality on the number line and the variable is on the right side of the inequality sign.

1. Teacher poses many problems using Transparency 1.1.4.

2. Partner A compares the two numbers and writes the problem inserting the correct inequality symbol. Then he/she writes the expression as a sentence as the inequality would be read from left to right. He/she writes a second sentence as the inequality would be read from right to left.

3. Partner B watches, listens, checks, and praises.

4. Partner B repeats step 2 for the next problem.

▶ **Structure**
· RallyCoach

▶ **Materials**
· Transparency 1.1.4
· 1 sheet of paper and pencil per pair of students

5. Partner A watches, listens, checks, and praises.

6. Repeat for remaining problems starting at step 2.

ACTIVITY
5 COMPARE ME AGAIN

Numeric

Setup:
Blackline 1.1.5 needs to be copied onto two different colors of cardstock—one for the whole number cards and one for the inequality cards, then cut into individual cards. Cards are distributed to each team of students.

1. Teammate 1 mixes up the whole number cards and places them in a stack on the table. The inequality cards are in a stack, faceup.

2. Each teammate draws a whole number card.

3. Teammate 2 arranges the drawn whole number cards with the correct inequality cards he/she has chosen from the inequality card stack. Teammate 2 explains to his/her team why the cards are placed in that order. The teammate checks for consensus.

4. The teammates show agreement or lack of agreement with thumbs up or down.

5. If there is agreement, the students celebrate and the steps 2–5 are repeated rotating one teammate each time. If not, the teammates discuss the response until there is

▶ **Structure**
· RoundTable Consensus

▶ **Materials**
· 1 set of Whole Number and Inequality Cards (Blackline 1.1.5) per team

agreement and then they celebrate. If no agreement is reached, the cards are set aside to be discussed later.

6. Repeat steps 2–5, rotating 1 teammate each time.

Chapter 1: Whole Numbers

Lesson One

ACTIVITY

6 PLOT MY POINT

▶ Structure
• RallyCoach

▶ Materials
• Transparency 1.1.6
• 2 sheets of graph paper, 1 ruler, and pencil per pair of students

Graphic

This activity does for the coordinate plane what activity 3 did for the number line. Students will plot the same point on different coordinate planes. Each coordinate plane will have a different scale on the axes. This activity will also be repeated for the integer, decimal, and fraction chapters. By spiraling this activity, the students should master plotting points.

1. Teacher poses many problems using Transparency 1.1.6.

2. Partner A graphs the point in the first problem on a coordinate plane, using any scale he/she chooses.

3. Partner B watches, listens, checks, and praises.

4. Partner B graphs the same point on a different coordinate plane, using a different scale of his/her choice.

5. Partner A watches, listens, checks, and praises.

6. Repeat until three graphs are graphed for problem one.

7. Repeat for remaining problems starting at step 2.

ACTIVITY

7 AM I DIVISIBLE?

▶ Structure
• Quiz-Quiz-Trade

▶ Materials
• 1 set of Whole Number Cards Blackline 1.1.5 (1 card per student)

Numeric

Setup:
The cards need to be copied onto cardstock and cut into individual cards. Cards are distributed to the students, 1 card per student.

1. StandUp–HandUp–PairUp.

2. Partner A quizzes his/her partner, asking what numbers evenly divide the number on his/her card.

3. Partner B answers.

4. Partner A praises or coaches.

5. Switch roles.

6. Partners trade cards.

7. Repeat steps 1–6 as many times as the teacher chooses.

Cooperative Learning and Pre-Algebra: Becky Bride
Kagan Publishing • 1 (800) 933-2667 • www.KaganOnline.com

ACTIVITY

8 PRIME OR COMPOSITE?

Numeric

Setup:
The cards need to be copied onto cardstock and cut into individual cards. Cards are distributed to the students, 1 card per student.

1. StandUp–Hand Up–Pair Up.

2. Partner A quizzes his/her partner, asking whether the number on his/her card is composite or prime and then justifies his/her answer.

3. Partner B answers.

4. Partner A praises or coaches.

5. Switch roles.

6. Partners trade cards.

7. Repeat steps 1–6 as many times as the teacher chooses.

▶ **Structure**
• Quiz-Quiz-Trade

▶ **Materials**
• 1 set of Whole Number Cards Blackline 1.1.5 (1 card per student)

ACTIVITY

9 EXPLORING TERMS AND FACTORS

Numeric

Solo
1. Individually, each student completes the exploration.

Pair Consensus
2. For each problem on the investigation, each student shares with his/her partner, using RallyRobin, his/her response. They discuss the problems that they disagree on, trying to come to consensus on the correct response. They mark the problems they can't reach consensus on so they can focus on them during the team phase. Encourage the students to add to their responses if their partner verbalizes an understanding they did not see.

Team Consensus
3. Each pair shares their responses, using RallyRobin, with the other pair in their team, augmenting their responses if necessary. When the teams are through sharing, each student should have a detailed, complete summary.

▶ **Structure**
• Solo-Pair Consensus-Team Consensus

▶ **Materials**
• Blackline 1.1.7 per student
• 1 pencil per student

ACTIVITY
10 FACTORS OR TERMS?

▶ **Structure**
· RallyRobin

▶ **Materials**
· Transparency 1.1.8

Numeric

1. Teacher poses multiple problems using Transparency 1.1.8.

2. In pairs, students take turns orally stating whether the expression in the problem has factors or terms and justifies his/her answer.

ACTIVITY
11 REWRITE ME

▶ **Structure**
· RallyCoach

▶ **Materials**
· Transparency 1.1.8
· 1 sheet of paper and pencil per pair of students

Numeric

1. Teacher poses many problems using Transparency 1.1.8.

2. Partner A writes the first problem using multiplication or exponents.

3. Partner B watches, listens, checks, and praises.

4. Partner B writes the next problem using multiplication or exponents.

5. Partner A watches, listens, checks, and praises.

6. Repeat for remaining problems starting at step 2.

ACTIVITY
12 EXPLORING ADD/SUBTRACT VS. MULTIPLY/DIVIDE

▶ **Structure**
· Solo-Pair Consensus-Team Consensus

▶
Materials
· Blackline 1.1.9 per student
· 1 pencil per student
· 1 scientific calculator per student

Exploratory

Solo
1. Individually, each student completes the exploration.

Pair Consensus
2. For each problem on the investigation, each student shares with his/her partner, using RallyRobin, his/her response. They discuss the problems that they disagree on, trying to come to consensus on the correct response. They mark the problems they can't reach consensus on so

they can focus on them during the team phase. Encourage the students to add to their responses if their partner verbalizes an understanding they did not see.

Team Consensus
3. Each pair shares their responses, using RallyRobin, with the other pair in their team, augmenting their responses if necessary. When the teams are through sharing, each student should have a detailed, complete summary.

Cooperative Learning and Pre-Algebra: Becky Bride
Kagan Publishing • 1 (800) 933-2667 • www.KaganOnline.com

ACTIVITY
13 WHAT DO I DO FIRST?

Numeric

1. Teacher poses multiple problems using Transparency 1.1.10.

2. In pairs, students take turns orally stating which operation in the problem is completed first and justifies his/her answer.

▶ **Structure**
• RallyRobin

▶ **Materials**
• Transparency 1.1.10

ACTIVITY
14 EVALUATE ME

Numeric

Setup:
In pairs, Student A is the Sage; Student B is the Scribe. Students fold a sheet of paper in half and each writes his/her name on one half.

1. The Sage gives the Scribe step-by-step instructions on how to solve problem one.

2. The Scribe records the Sage's solution step-by-step in writing on the Sage's side of the paper.

3. If the Sage is correct, the Scribe praises the Sage. Otherwise, the Scribe coaches, then praises.

4. Students switch roles for the next problem.

▶ **Structure**
• Sage-N-Scribe

▶ **Materials**
• Transparency 1.1.10
• 1 sheet of paper and pencil per pair of students

ACTIVITY
15 EXPLORING MULTIPLY/DIVIDE VS. EXPONENTS

Exploratory

Solo
1. Individually, each student completes the exploration.

Pair Consensus
2. For each problem on the investigation, each student shares with his/her partner, using RallyRobin, his/her response. They discuss the problems that they disagree on, trying to come to consensus on the correct response. They mark the problems they can't reach consensus on so they can focus on them during the team phase. Encourage the students to add to their responses if their partner verbalizes an understanding they did not see.

Team Consensus
3. Each pair shares their responses, using RallyRobin, with the other pair in their team, augmenting their responses if necessary. When the teams are through sharing, each student should have a detailed, complete summary.

▶ **Structure**
• Solo-Pair Consensus-Team Consensus

▶ **Materials**
• Blackline 1.1.11 per student
• 1 sheet of paper and pencil per student
• 1 scientific calculator per student

ACTIVITY

16 WHAT DO I DO FIRST? TAKE 2

▶ **Structure**
• RallyRobin

Materials
▶ • Transparency 1.1.12

Numeric

1. Teacher poses multiple problems using Transparency 1.1.12.

2. In pairs, students take turns orally stating which operation in the problem is completed first and justifies his/her answer.

ACTIVITY

17 EVALUATE ME—TAKE 2

▶ **Structure**
• Sage-N-Scribe

▶ **Materials**
• Transparency 1.1.12
• 1 sheet of paper and pencil per pair of students

Numeric

Setup:
In pairs, Student A is the Sage; Student B is the Scribe. Students fold a sheet of paper in half and each writes his/her name on one half.

1. The Sage gives the Scribe step-by-step instructions on how to solve problem one.

2. The Scribe records the Sage's solution step-by-step in writing on the Sage's side of the paper.

3. If the Sage is correct, the Scribe praises the Sage. Otherwise, the Scribe coaches, then praises.

4. Students switch roles for the next problem.

ACTIVITY

18 EVALUATE ME—TAKE 3

▶ **Structure**
• Sage-N-Scribe

▶ **Materials**
• Transparency 1.1.13
• 1 sheet of paper and pencil per pair of students

Numeric

Setup:
In pairs, Student A is the Sage; Student B is the Scribe. Students fold a sheet of paper in half and each writes his/her name on one half.

1. The Sage gives the Scribe step-by-step instructions on how to solve problem one.

2. The Scribe records the Sage's solution step-by-step in writing on the Sage's side of the paper.

3. If the Sage is correct, the Scribe praises the Sage. Otherwise, the Scribe coaches, then praises.

4. Students switch roles for the next problem.

Cooperative Learning and Pre-Algebra: Becky Bride
Kagan Publishing • 1 (800) 933-2667 • www.KaganOnline.com

ACTIVITY 19 — EXPLORING THE ROLE OF GROUPING SYMBOLS

Exploratory

Solo
1. Individually, each student completes the exploration.

Pair Consensus
2. For each problem on the investigation, each student shares with his/her partner, using RallyRobin, his/her response. They discuss the problems that they disagree on, trying to come to consensus on the correct response. They mark the problems they can't reach consensus on so

they can focus on them during the team phase. Encourage the students to add to their responses if their partner verbalizes an understanding they did not see.

Team Consensus
3. Each pair shares their responses, using RallyRobin, with the other pair in their team, augmenting their responses if necessary. When the teams are through sharing, each student should have a detailed, complete summary.

▶ **Structure**
• Solo-Pair Consensus-Team Consensus

▶ **Materials**
• Blackline 1.1.14 per student
• 1 pencil per student
• 1 scientific calculator per student

ACTIVITY 20 — PROCESSING ALL THE OPERATIONS

Numeric

Setup:
In pairs, Student A is the Sage; Student B is the Scribe. Students fold a sheet of paper in half and each writes his/her name on one half.

1. The Sage gives the Scribe step-by-step instructions on how to solve problem one.

2. The Scribe records the Sage's solution step-by-step in writing on the Sage's side of the paper.

3. If the Sage is correct, the Scribe praises the Sage. Otherwise, the Scribe coaches, then praises.

4. Students switch roles for the next problem.

▶ **Structure**
• Sage-N-Scribe

▶ **Materials**
• Transparency 1.1.15
• 1 sheet of paper and pencil per pair of students

Chapter 1: Whole Numbers

Lesson One

Cooperative Learning and Pre-Algebra: Becky Bride
Kagan Publishing • 1 (800) 933-2667 • www.KaganOnline.com

11

21 FIND MY MATCH

▶ **Structure**
- Mix-N-Match

▶ **Materials**
- 1 set of Mix-N-Match Cards for the class (Blackline 1.1.16)
- 1 sheet of paper and pencil per student

Numeric

Setup:
The cards need to be copied onto cardstock and cut into individual cards. Cards are distributed to the students, 1 card per student.

1. With a card in their hand, each student mixes around the room. Each finds a partner and Partner A asks what the solution is to the problem on his/her card.

2. Partner B answers, writing his/her response on paper if necessary.

3. Partner A praises or coaches.

4. Switch roles.

5. Partners trade cards.

6. Partners split up and repeat steps 1–6 a number of times.

7. Teacher calls "Freeze."

8. Students freeze, hide their cards, and think of their match.

9. Students move to the center of the room, find their match, and quickly move away from the center of the room with their new partner.

Management Tips:
Use music to begin and end the Mix-N-Match. The students may find their matches talking or silently. Once a student finds their match, ask the pair to stand along the perimeter of the room. To collect the cards, ask that both cards be given to one member of each pair. Then as the students return to their seats, they will hand the pairs of cards to the teacher. This way the matches are together, so when the next class comes in with a different number of students, the teacher will be able to ensure that matches can be made when the cards are distributed.

22 WHERE DO THE OPERATIONS GO?

▶ **Structure**
- RallyCoach

▶ **Materials**
- Transparency 1.1.17
- 1 sheet of paper and pencil per pair of students

Numeric

1. Teacher poses many problems using Transparency 1.1.17.

2. Partner A writes the first problem placing the appropriate operation symbols to get the requested answer.

3. Partner B watches, listens, checks, and praises.

4. Partner B writes the next problem placing the appropriate operation symbols in the correct places to get the requested answer.

5. Partner A watches, listens, checks, and praises.

6. Repeat for remaining problems starting at step 2.

Cooperative Learning and Pre-Algebra: Becky Bride
Kagan Publishing • 1 (800) 933-2667 • www.KaganOnline.com

ACTIVITY
23 WHAT DID WE LEARN?

Synthesis

1. Each teammate signs his/her name in the upper right corner of the team paper with the color pen/pencil he/she is using.

2. One teammate writes *"Whole Numbers"* in the center of the team paper in a rectangle.

3. Teammate 1 shares with the team one core concept he/she learned in the unit.

4. The student checks for consensus.

5. The teammates show agreement or lack of agreement with thumbs up or down.

6. If there is agreement, the students celebrate and the teammate records the core concept on the graphic organizer, connecting it with a line to the main idea—*Whole Numbers*. If not, teammates discuss the response until there is agreement and then they celebrate.

7. Play continues with the next student's core concept, until all core concepts are exhausted.

8. Repeat steps 3–7 with teammates adding details to each core concept and making bridges between related ideas.

▶ **Structure**
· RoundTable Consensus

▶ **Materials**
· 1 large sheet of paper per team
· 1 different color pen or pencil for each student in the team

Chapter 1: Whole Numbers

Lesson One

Cooperative Learning and Pre-Algebra: Becky Bride
Kagan Publishing • 1 (800) 933-2667 • www.KaganOnline.com

13

ACTIVITY 1 ⟨AN YOU DEFINE ME?

Structure: Solo-Pair Consensus-Team Consensus

The set of natural numbers is the set {1, 2, 3, 4, 5, 6, . . .}.
The set of whole numbers is the set {0, 1, 2, 3, 4, 5, 6, . . .}.

1. Describe how the two sets are similar.

2. Describe how the two sets are different.

3. Describe the type of numbers, which you have studied about in previous years, that are missing in both of these sets.

4. Write your own definition for the set of natural numbers.

5. Write your own definition for the set of whole numbers.

Cooperative Learning and Pre-Algebra: Becky Bride
Kagan Publishing • 1 (800) 933-2667 • www.KaganOnline.com

ACTIVITY
2 **CLASSIFY ME**

Structure: RallyCoach

Classify each number by stating the set(s) of numbers to which it belongs.

1. 10

2. 0.37

3. 2

4. 209

5. 0

6. 1,215

7. $\frac{3}{4}$

8. 20

Answers:
1. natural, whole, real
2. real
3. natural, whole, real
4. natural, whole, real
5. whole, real
6. natural, whole, real
7. real
8. natural, whole, real

ACTIVITY
3

HOW MANY WAYS CAN YOU GRAPH ME?

Structure: RallyCoach

Graph each number on a number line, changing the scale of the number line each time it is graphed.

1. 18

2. 44

3. 72

4. 48

Answers will vary.

Cooperative Learning and Pre-Algebra: Becky Bride
Kagan Publishing • 1 (800) 933-2667 • www.KaganOnline.com

COMPARE ME

Structure: RallyCoach

For each problem:
a. Write a number sentence using the correct inequality symbol.
b. Using words, write a sentence as the inequality reads from left to right.
c. Using words, write a sentence as the inequality reads from right to left.

1. 5   9   2. 8   0

3. 37   21   4. 41   83

5. 0   19   6. 95   89

Answers:
1. $5 < 9$; Five is less than nine; Nine is greater than five.
2. $8 > 0$; Eight is greater than zero; Zero is less than eight.
3. $37 > 21$; Thirty-seven is greater than twenty-one; Twenty-one is less than thirty-seven.
4. $41 < 83$; Forty-one is less than eighty-three; Eighty-three is greater than forty-one.
5. $0 < 19$; Zero is less than nineteen; Nineteen is greater than zero.
6. $95 > 89$; Ninety-five is greater than eighty-nine; Eighty-nine is less than ninety-five.

ACTIVITY 5

COMPARE ME AGAIN

Structure: RoundTable Consensus

Whole Number Cards

0	1	2	3
4	5	6	7
8	9	10	11
12	13	14	15
16	17	18	19

Cooperative Learning and Pre-Algebra: Becky Bride
Kagan Publishing • 1 (800) 933-2667 • www.KaganOnline.com

ACTIVITY 5

COMPARE ME AGAIN

Structure: RoundTable Consensus

Whole Number Cards

20	**21**	**22**	**23**
24	**25**	**26**	**27**
28	**29**	**30**	**31**
32	**33**	**34**	**35**
36	**37**	**38**	**39**

ACTIVITY
5

COMPARE ME AGAIN

Structure: RoundTable Consensus
Inequality Cards

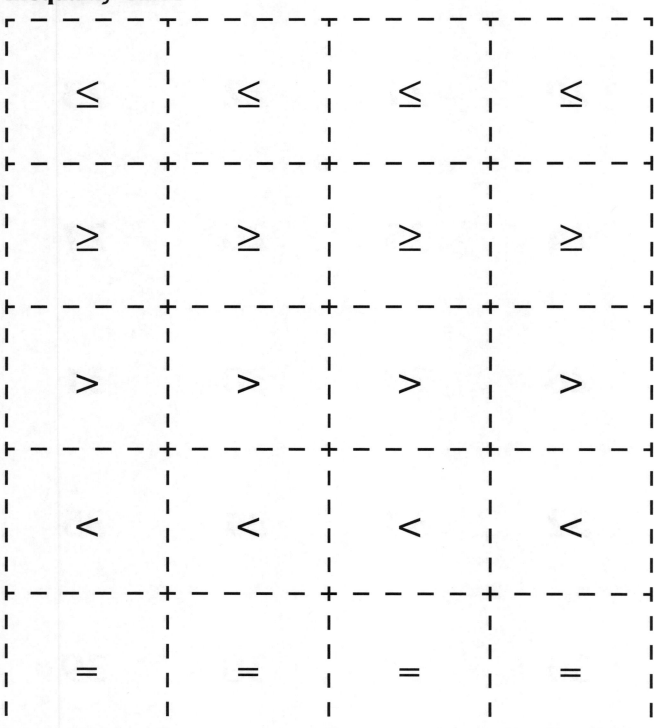

Cooperative Learning and Pre-Algebra: Becky Bride
Kagan Publishing • 1 (800) 933-2667 • www.KaganOnline.com

6 PLOT MY POINT

Structure: RallyCoach

Plot each point on a different coordinate plane using different scales on the axes.

1. (3, 6)

2. (5, 10)

3. (45, 27)

4. (32, 18)

Answers will vary.

ACTIVITY
9 **EXPLORING TERMS AND FACTORS**

Structure: Solo-Pair Consensus-Team Consensus

1. Given $2 + 2 + 2 + 2 + 2 = 2 \times 5$, what does the expression 2×5 tell you about the number 2?

2. Given $5 + 5 = 5 \times 2$, what does the expression 5×2 tell you about the number 5?

3. Given $3 + 3 + 3 + 3 = 3 \times 4$, what does the expression 3×4 tell you about the number 3?

4. Given $7 + 7 + 7 = 7 \times 3$, what does the expression 7×3 tell you about the number 7?

5. Look at the left side of each equation above. What is similar about each one?

6. The 2's, 5's, 3's, and 7's on the left side of the equations above are called terms. Explain what a term is.

7. Given $6 \times 6 \times 6 \times 6 \times 6 = 6^5$, what does 6^5 tell you about the number 6?

Cooperative Learning and Pre-Algebra: Becky Bride
Kagan Publishing • 1 (800) 933-2667 • www.KaganOnline.com

ACTIVITY 9 EXPLORING TERMS AND FACTORS

Structure: Solo-Pair Consensus-Team Consensus

8. Given $7 \times 7 \times 7 \times 7 \times 7 \times 7 \times 7 \times 7 \times 7 = 7^9$, what does 7^9 tell you about the number 7?

9. Given $3 \times 3 \times 3 \times 3 = 3^4$, what does 3^4 tell you about the number 3?

10. Given $8 \times 8 \times 8 \times 8 \times 8 = 8^5$, what does 8^5 tell you about the number 8?

11. Look at the left side of the equation in problems 7–10. What is similar about them?

12. The 6's, 7's, 3's, and 8's on the left side of the equations above are called factors. The little raised number on the right side is called an exponent. Explain what a *factor* is.

13. Explain the difference between a *factor* and a *term*.

10 & 11   FACTORS OR TERMS? REWRITE ME

Structure: RallyRobin (Activity 10)
Structure: RallyCoach (Activity 11)

Directions:

Activity 10: State whether the expression has factors or terms.

Activity 11: Rewrite each expression using multiplication or exponents.

1. $13 \times 13 \times 13 \times 13 \times 13 \times 13$

2. $9 + 9 + 9 + 9$

3. $24 + 24 + 24 + 24 + 24 + 24 + 24$

4. $1 \times 1 \times 1 \times 1 \times 1 \times 1 \times 1 \times 1 \times 1 \times 1$

5. $2 \times 2 \times 2 \times 2 \times 2 \times 2 \times 2$

6. $16 + 16 + 16 + 16 + 16 + 16 + 16 + 16 + 16$

Answers:

1. factors; 13^6	2. terms; 9×4	3. terms; 24×7
4. factors; 1^{10}	5. factors; 2^7	6. terms; 16×9

Cooperative Learning and Pre-Algebra: Becky Bride
Kagan Publishing • 1 (800) 933-2667 • www.KaganOnline.com

ACTIVITY 12 EXPLORING ADD/SUBTRACT VS. MULTIPLY/DIVIDE

Structure: Solo-Pair Consensus-Team Consensus

1. a) Enter the problem: 2 + 3 × 4 = ? into your calculator and record the answer below.

   b) Without a calculator, add 2 and 3, then multiply the result by 4. Record your answer and work below. Does it match the answer found in part a?

   c) Without a calculator, multiply 3 and 4, then add 2 to the result. Record your answer and work below. Does it match the answer found in part a?

   d) To get the answer in part a, which operation had to be performed first?

2. a) Enter the problem: 15 − 6 × 2 = ? into your calculator and record the answer below.

   b) Without a calculator, subtract 6 from 15, then multiply the result by 2. Record your answer and work below. Does it match the answer found in part a?

   c) Without a calculator, multiply 6 and 2, then subtract the result from 15. Record your answer and work below. Does it match the answer found in part a?

   d) To get the answer in part a, which operation had to be performed first?

EXPLORING ADD/SUBTRACT VS. MULTIPLY/DIVIDE

ACTIVITY 12

Structure: Solo-Pair Consensus-Team Consensus

3. a) Enter the problem: $8 \cdot 7 - 5 = ?$ into your calculator and record the answer below.

   b) Without a calculator, multiply 8 and 7, then subtract 5 from the result. Record your answer and work below. Does it match the answer found in part a?

   c) Without a calculator, subtract 5 from 7, then multiply the result by 8. Record your answer and work below. Does it match the answer found in part a?

   d) To get the answer in part a, which operation had to be performed first?

4. a) Enter the problem: $5 \cdot 7 + 2 = ?$ into your calculator and record the answer below.

   b) Without a calculator, multiply 5 and 7, then add 2 to the result. Record your answer and work below. Does it match the answer found in part a?

   c) Without a calculator, add 7 and 2, then multiply the result by 5. Record your answer and work below. Does it match the answer found in part a?

   d) To get the answer in part a, which operation had to be performed first?

Cooperative Learning and Pre-Algebra: Becky Bride
Kagan Publishing • 1 (800) 933-2667 • www.KaganOnline.com

ACTIVITY 12 — EXPLORING ADD/SUBTRACT VS. MULTIPLY/DIVIDE

Structure: Solo-Pair Consensus-Team Consensus

5. a) Enter the problem: $26 - 3 \times 5 = ?$ into your calculator and record the answer below.

   b) Without a calculator, subtract 3 from 26, then multiply the result by 5. Record your answer and work below. Does it match the answer found in part a?

   c) Without a calculator, multiply 3 and 5, then subtract the result from 26. Record your answer and work below. Does it match the answer found in part a?

   d) To get the answer in part a, which operation had to be performed first?

6. In problems 1–5, which operation was always performed first?

7. a) Enter the problem: $18 \div 2 + 4 = ?$ into your calculator and record the answer below.

   b) Without a calculator, divide 18 by 2, then add 4 to the result. Record your answer and work below. Does it match the answer found in part a?

   c) Without a calculator, add 2 and 4, divide 18 by the result. Record your answer and work below. Does it match the answer found in part a?

   d) To get the answer in part a, which operation had to be performed first?

EXPLORING ADD/SUBTRACT VS. MULTIPLY/DIVIDE

Structure: Solo-Pair Consensus-Team Consensus

8. a) Enter the problem: 9 + 12 ÷ 3 = ? into your calculator and record the answer below.

   b) Without a calculator, add 9 and 12, then divide the result by 3. Record your answer and work below. Does it match the answer found in part a?

   c) Without a calculator, divide 12 by 3, then add 9 to the result. Record your answer and work below. Does it match the answer found in part a?

   d) To get the answer in part a, which operation had to be performed first?

9. a) Enter the problem: 28 −14 ÷ 7 = ? into your calculator and record the answer below.

   b) Without a calculator, subtract 14 from 28, then divide the result by 7. Record your answer and work below. Does it match the answer found in part a?

   c) Without a calculator, divide 14 by 7, then subtract the result from 28. Record your answer and work below. Does it match the answer found in part a?

   d) To get the answer in part a, which operation had to be performed first?

Cooperative Learning and Pre-Algebra: Becky Bride
Kagan Publishing • 1 (800) 933-2667 • www.KaganOnline.com

EXPLORING ADD/SUBTRACT VS. MULTIPLY/DIVIDE

ACTIVITY 12

Structure: Solo-Pair Consensus-Team Consensus

10. a) Enter the problem: $36 \div 6 + 6 = ?$ into your calculator and record the answer below.

    b) Without a calculator, divide 36 by 6, then add 6 to the result. Record your answer and work below. Does it match the answer found in part a?

    c) Without a calculator, add 6 and 6, then divide 36 by the result. Record your answer and work below. Does it match the answer found in part a?

    d) To get the answer in part a, which operation had to be performed first?

11. a) Enter the problem: $24 - 15 \div 3 = ?$ into your calculator and record the answer below.

    b) Without a calculator, subtract 15 from 24, then divide the result by 3. Record your answer and work below. Does it match the answer found in part a?

    c) Without a calculator, divide 15 by 3, then subtract the result from 24. Record your answer and work below. Does it match the answer found in part a?

    d) To get the answer in part a, which operation had to be performed first?

12. In problems 7–11, which operation was always preformed first?

13. Summarize what you have learned about which order the operations addition/subtraction and multiplication/division are performed.

ACTIVITIES
13 & 14 WHAT DO I DO FIRST? EVALUATE ME

Structure: RallyRobin (Activity 13)
Structure: Sage-N-Scribe (Activity 14)

Directions:

Activity 13: State which pair of numbers and which operation is completed first.
Activity 14: Evaluate each problem.

1. $12 - 3 \times 2$

2. $12 \div 4 - 1$

3. $4 \times 5 + 3$

4. $17 - 3 \times 2$

5. $20 + 4 \div 2$

6. $6 \times 7 - 3$

7. $30 \div 3 + 2$

8. $15 + 9 \div 3$

9. $15 - 12 \div 3$

10. $13 + 3 \times 2$

Answers:
Activity 13
1. 3×2	2. $12 \div 4$	3. 4×5	4. 3×2	5. $4 \div 2$
6. 6×7	7. $30 \div 3$	8. $9 \div 3$	9. $12 \div 3$	10. 3×2

Activity 14
1. 6	2. 2	3. 23	4. 11	5. 22
6. 39	7. 12	8. 18	9. 11	10. 19

Cooperative Learning and Pre-Algebra: Becky Bride
Kagan Publishing • 1 (800) 933-2667 • www.KaganOnline.com

EXPLORING MULTIPLY/DIVIDE VS. EXPONENTS

Structure: Solo-Pair Consensus-Team Consensus

For this investigation, you will need a scientific calculator.

1. a) Enter the problem: $4 \cdot 3^2 = ?$ into your calculator and record the answer below.

    b) Without a calculator, multiply 4 by 3, then square the result. Record your work and answer below. Does the answer match the answer in part a?

    c) Without a calculator, square 3, then multiply the result by 4. Record your work and answer below. Does the answer match the answer in part a?

    d) To get the answer in part a, which operation had to be performed first?

2. a) Enter the problem: $16 \div 4^2 = ?$ into your calculator and record the answer below.

    b) Without a calculator, divide 16 by 4, then square the result. Record your work and answer below. Does the answer match the answer in part a?

    c) Without a calculator, square 4, then divide 16 by the result. Record your work and answer below. Does the answer match the answer in part a?

    d) To get the answer in part a, which operation had to be performed first?

ACTIVITY 15 EXPLORING MULTIPLY/DIVIDE VS. EXPONENTS

Structure: Solo-Pair Consensus-Team Consensus

3. a) Enter the problem: $8 \div 2^3$ = ? into your calculator and record the answer below.

   b) Without a calculator, divide 8 by 2, then raise the result to the third power. Record your work and answer below. Does the answer match the answer in part a?

   c) Without a calculator, raise 2 to the third power, then divide 8 by the result. Record your work and answer below. Does the answer match the answer in part a?

   d) To get the answer in part a, which operation had to be performed first?

4. a) Enter the problem: $2^5 \cdot 4$ = ? into your calculator and record the answer below.

   b) Without a calculator, raise 2 to the fifth power, then multiply the result by 4. Record your work and answer below. Does the answer match the answer in part a?

   c) Without a calculator, multiply 2 by 4, then raise the result to the fifth power. Record your work and answer below. Does the answer match the answer in part a?

   d) To get the answer in part a, which operation had to be performed first?

Cooperative Learning and Pre-Algebra: Becky Bride
Kagan Publishing • 1 (800) 933-2667 • www.KaganOnline.com

ACTIVITY 15 EXPLORING MULTIPLY/DIVIDE VS. EXPONENTS

Structure: Solo-Pair Consensus-Team Consensus

5. a) Enter the problem: $6^2 \div 3 = ?$ into your calculator and record the answer below.

   b) Without a calculator, square 6, then divide the result by 3. Record your work and answer below. Does the answer match the answer in part a?

   c) Without a calculator, divide 6 by 3, then square the result. Record your work and answer below. Does the answer match the answer in part a?

   d) To get the answer in part a, which operation had to be performed first?

6. a) Enter the problem: $9^3 \div 3 = ?$ into your calculator and record the answer below.

   b) Without a calculator, divide 9 by 3, then raise the result to the third power. Record your work and answer below. Does the answer match the answer in part a?

   c) Without a calculator, raise 9 to the third power, then divide the result by 3. Record your work and answer below. Does the answer match the answer in part a?

   d) To get the answer in part a, which operation had to be performed first?

7. In problems 1–6, what operation was always performed first?

8. Summarize what you have learned about the order of the operations addition/subtraction, multiplication/division, and exponents.

ACTIVITIES
16 & 17 WHAT DO I DO FIRST?—TAKE 2
EVALUATE ME—TAKE 2

Structure: RallyRobin (Activity 16)
Structure: Sage-N-Scribe (Activity 17)

Directions:

Activity 16: State which pair of numbers and which operation will be evaluated first.
Activity 17: Evaluate each problem.

1. 2×5^3 2. $10^3 \div 5$

3. $4^2 \times 2$ 4. $24 \div 2^3$

5. $6^2 \div 3$ 6. 8×4^3

Answers:
Activity 16
1. 5^3 2. 10^3 3. 4^2 4. 2^3 5. 6^2 6. 4^3

Activity 17
1. 250   2. 200   3. 32   4. 3   5. 12   6. 512

Cooperative Learning and Pre-Algebra: Becky Bride
Kagan Publishing • 1 (800) 933-2667 • www.KaganOnline.com

Structure: Sage-N-Scribe

Evaluate each using the order of operations.

1. $24 + 2^3 \div 4$

2. $3^2 + 6 \div 3$

3. $30 - 12 \div 2^2$

4. $48 \div 4^2 + 8$

5. $60 - 50 \div 5^2$

6. $2^4 \times 3 \div 6$

7. $4^3 \div 2 \times 4 + 1$

8. $12 + 8 \div 2^2 - 5$

Answers:
1. 26	2. 11	3. 27	4. 11
5. 58	6. 8	7. 129	8. 9

EXPLORING THE ROLE OF GROUPING SYMBOLS

Structure: Solo-Pair Consensus-Team Consensus

For this investigation, you will need a scientific calculator.

1. a) Enter the problem: $5 \times (3 + 4) = ?$ into your calculator and record the answer below.

   b) Without a calculator, multiply 5 by 3, then add 4 to the result. Record your work and answer below. Does the answer match the answer in part a?

   c) Without a calculator, add 3 and 4, then multiply the result by 5. Record your work and answer below. Does the answer match the answer in part a?

   d) To get the answer in part a, which operation had to be performed first?

   e) What role did the parentheses play in the order in which the calculator performed the operations?

Cooperative Learning and Pre-Algebra: Becky Bride
Kagan Publishing • 1 (800) 933-2667 • www.KaganOnline.com

ACTIVITY 19 EXPLORING THE ROLE OF GROUPING SYMBOLS

Structure: Solo-Pair Consensus-Team Consensus

2. a) Enter the problem: $(15 - 6) \times 2 = ?$ into your calculator and record the answer below.

   b) Without a calculator, subtract 6 from 15, then multiply the result by 2. Record your work and answer below. Does the answer match the answer in part a?

   c) Without a calculator, multiply 6 and 2, then subtract the result from 15. Record your work and answer below. Does the answer match the answer in part a?

   d) To get the answer in part a, which operation had to be performed first?

   e) What role did the parentheses play in the order in which the calculator performed the operations?

3. a) Enter the problem: $8 \times (9 - 7) = ?$ into your calculator and record the answer below.

   b) Without a calculator, multiply 8 by 9, then subtract 7 from the result. Record your work and answer below. Does the answer match the answer in part a?

   c) Without a calculator, subtract 7 from 9, then multiply the result by 8. Record your work and answer below. Does the answer match the answer in part a?

   d) To get the answer in part a, which operation had to be performed first?

   e) What role did the parentheses play in the order in which the calculator performed the operations?

ACTIVITY 19

EXPLORING THE ROLE OF GROUPING SYMBOLS

Structure: Solo-Pair Consensus-Team Consensus

4. a) Enter the problem: $(5 + 2)^2 = ?$ into your calculator and record the answer below.

   b) Without a calculator, add 5 and 2, then square the result. Record your work and answer below. Does the answer match the answer in part a?

   c) Without a calculator, square 2, then add 5 to the result. Record your work and answer below. Does the answer match the answer in part a?

   d) To get the answer in part a, which operation had to be performed first?

   e) What role did the parentheses play in the order in which the calculator performed the operations?

5. a) Enter the problem: $18 \div (2 + 4) = ?$ into your calculator and record the answer below.

   b) Without a calculator, divide 18 by 2, then add 4 to the result. Record your work and answer below. Does the answer match the answer in part a?

   c) Without a calculator, add 2 and 4, then divide 18 by the result. Record your work and answer below. Does the answer match the answer in part a?

   d) To get the answer in part a, which operation had to be performed first?

   e) What role did the parentheses play in the order in which the calculator performed the operations?

Cooperative Learning and Pre-Algebra: Becky Bride
Kagan Publishing • 1 (800) 933-2667 • www.KaganOnline.com

ACTIVITY 19 EXPLORING THE ROLE OF GROUPING SYMBOLS

Structure: Solo-Pair Consensus-Team Consensus

6. a) Enter the problem: $(9 + 12) \div 3 = ?$ into your calculator and record the answer below.

   b) Without a calculator, add 9 and 12, then divide the result by 3. Record your work and answer below. Does the answer match the answer in part a?

   c) Without a calculator, divide 12 by 3, then add 9 to the result. Record your work and answer below. Does the answer match the answer in part a?

   d) To get the answer in part a, which operation had to be performed first?

   e) What role did the parentheses play in the order in which the calculator performed the operations?

7. a) Enter the problem: $(28 - 14) \div 7 = ?$ into your calculator and record the answer below.

   b) Without a calculator, subtract 14 from 28, then divide the result by 7. Record your work and answer below. Does the answer match the answer in part a?

   c) Without a calculator, divide 14 by 7, then subtract the result from 28. Record your work and answer below. Does the answer match the answer in part a?

   d) To get the answer in part a, which operation had to be performed first?

   e) What role did the parentheses play in the order in which the calculator performed the operations?

ACTIVITY 19 EXPLORING THE ROLE OF GROUPING SYMBOLS

Structure: Solo-Pair Consensus-Team Consensus

8. a) Enter the problem: $\dfrac{48}{(8-6)}$ = ? into your calculator and record the answer below.

b) Without a calculator, divide 48 by 8, then subtract the result from 6. Record your work and answer below. Does the answer match the answer in part a?

c) Without a calculator, subtract 6 from 8 then divide 48 by the result. Record your work and answer below. Does the answer match the answer in part a?

d) To get the answer in part a, which operation had to be performed first?

e) What role did the parentheses play in the order in which the calculator performed the operations?

9. a) Enter the problem: $\dfrac{(15-9)}{3}$ = ? into your calculator and record the answer below.

b) Without a calculator, subtract 9 from 15, then divide the result by 3. Record your work and answer below. Does the answer match the answer in part a?

c) Without a calculator, divide 9 by 3, then subtract the result from 15. Record your work and answer below. Does the answer match the answer in part a?

d) To get the answer in part a, which operation had to be performed first?

e) What role did the parentheses play in the order in which the calculator performed the operations?

Cooperative Learning and Pre-Algebra: Becky Bride
Kagan Publishing • 1 (800) 933-2667 • www.KaganOnline.com

EXPLORING THE ROLE OF GROUPING SYMBOLS

Structure: Solo-Pair Consensus-Team Consensus

10. a) Enter the problem: $\dfrac{24}{(4 + 2)} = ?$ into your calculator and record the answer below.

    b) Without a calculator, divide 24 by 4, then add 2 to the result. Record your work and answer below. Does the answer match the answer in part a?

    c) Without a calculator, add 4 and 2, then divide 24 by the result. Record your work and answer below. Does the answer match the answer in part a?

    d) To get the answer in part a, which operation had to be performed first?

    e) What role did the parentheses play in the order in which the calculator performed the operations?

11. Summarize what you have learned about the role of grouping symbols and the order that operations are performed.

12. Based on all the investigations you have done on order of operations, summarize these investigations by making a list of the order that operations are performed.

ACTIVITY

20 PROCESSING ALL THE OPERATIONS

Structure: Sage-N-Scribe

Evaluate each problem using order of operations.

1. $14 - (5 + 3) \div 2$

2. $9 + \dfrac{10}{2 + 3} + 4^2$

3. $3(4 - 1) + 12$

4. $(5 + 6)^2 - 2^3$

5. $\dfrac{28}{10 - 3} - 4$

6. $2(6^2 - 10)$

7. $12 - \dfrac{6 + 9}{3} - 1$

8. $24 - 2^2(8 - 5)$

Answers:
1. 10   2. 27   3. 21   4. 113
5. 0   6. 52   7. 6   8. 12

Cooperative Learning and Pre-Algebra: Becky Bride
Kagan Publishing • 1 (800) 933-2667 • www.KaganOnline.com

21 FIND MY MATCH

Structure: Mix-N-Match

$13 - 10 \div 2$	$4^2 - 2(1 + 3)$
$3^2 + \dfrac{16}{1 + 7}$	$5 - 2 + 2^3$
$42 \div 3 + 2^2$	$4^2 + \dfrac{5 + 9}{7}$
$20 - 4(2 + 3)$	$6^2 - 4(18 \div 2)$
$(1 + 4)^2 - 15$	$(1 + 5 \times 3) - 6$
$\dfrac{24}{2 + 4} + 2 \times 4$	$(2^4 - 10) \cdot 2$
$3 + 4(5) - 6$	$\dfrac{4 + 16}{5} + 13$
$6(8 - 5) \div 2$	$10 \div 2 + 2^2$

ACTIVITY
21 FIND MY MATCH

Structure: Mix-N-Match

$\dfrac{18+6}{2+4} - 3$	$4(3+1) \div 2^4$
$29 - 6(2) + 3$	$7(2+1) - 1$
$10 - \dfrac{32}{7+1}$	$(7^2 - 7) \div 7$
$1 + \dfrac{9^2}{5^2 + 2}$	$72 \div 9 - (3+1)$
$5(15 - 3 \times 4)$	$48 \div 4^2 + 12$
$28 - (7+3) \div 2$	$40 - 5^2 + 2^3$
$(10^2 + 8) \div 2$	$8(4+5) - 18$
$14 \div (3+4) + 28$	$\dfrac{20}{7-5} + 2^2(5)$

Cooperative Learning and Pre-Algebra: Becky Bride
Kagan Publishing • 1 (800) 933-2667 • www.KaganOnline.com

21 FIND MY MATCH

Structure: Mix-N-Match

$(19 - 4)(2) + 8$	$7^2 - (2 + 7) - 2$
$25 - 6 \div 2(3)$	$36 - 8 \div 2 \times 5$
$2^2 \times 10 \div 8$	$\dfrac{10^2}{2 + 3} \div 4$
$24 - 12 \div 4$	$5^2 - 2^2$

22 WHERE DO THE OPERATIONS GO?

Structure: RallyCoach

Use the numbers below and the operations +, −, ×, ÷, grouping symbols, and exponents to get the answer requested. The numbers are not necessarily in the order that they are to be used.

1. 3, 3, 4, 6; answer 17

2. 3, 4, 5, 21; answer 1

3. 1, 2, 3, 40; answer 80

4. 2, 3, 5, 12; answer 13

Answers:

1. $3^3 - (4 + 6)$ 2. $\dfrac{3 + 21}{4} - 5$

3. $40 \div 2(3 + 1)$ 4. $12 + 2(3) - 5$

Cooperative Learning and Pre-Algebra: Becky Bride
Kagan Publishing • 1 (800) 933-2667 • www.KaganOnline.com

LESSON 2
EXPRESSIONS

This lesson begins with students reading an inequality from left to right and then from right to left. To cut down on overlap between this book and the *Cooperative Learning and Algebra 1* book, I did not repeat the vocabulary development. Vocabulary development is extremely important and I urge you to use the activities for this development from the Algebra 1 book. Several activities give students the opportunity to practice interpreting inequality expressions. Activities follow to practice graphing on a number line. Factors and terms are revisited using expressions. Order of operations is reinforced as students evaluate expressions. The lesson ends with applications of expressions. For exploratory activities on like and unlike terms, see the Algebra 1 book. All coefficients and answers in this lesson are whole numbers.

ACTIVITY

READ ME TWO WAYS

Algebraic

1. Teacher poses multiple problems using Transparency 1.2.1.

2. In pairs, students take turns orally reading the expression in the problem from left to right and then from right to left. For the last four problems, the students will read beginning with the variable.

▶ **Structure**
• RallyRobin

▶ **Materials**
• Transparency 1.2.1

ACTIVITY

GIVE AN EXAMPLE

Algebraic

1. Teacher poses multiple problems using Transparency 1.2.1.

2. In pairs, students take turns orally stating a number that makes the inequality true.

▶ **Structure**
• RallyRobin

▶ **Materials**
• Transparency 1.2.1

ACTIVITY 3
WHERE DO I BELONG?

▶ **Structure**
· RoundRobin

▶ **Materials**
· Transparency 1.2.2
· 1 set of Whole Number Cards (Blackline 1.1.5) per team
· 1 sheet of paper and pencil per team

Algebraic

Setup:
Teacher poses many problems with Transparency 1.2.2. Give each team a set of whole number cards. Teammate 1 mixes up the cards. Teammate 2 deals the cards until all cards are gone. Teammate 3 takes the paper, folds it in fourths, and copies the inequalities on Transparency 1.2.2 into the appropriate quadrants of the paper.

1. Teammate 4 takes one of his/her cards and places it on the paper in the quadrant it belongs explaining to his/her teammates why he/she made that choice.

2. If the card is correctly placed, the teammates celebrate, otherwise they coach then celebrate.

3. Repeat steps 1–2 for the remaining cards, rotating one teammate each time.

ACTIVITY 4
GRAPH MY INEQUALITY

▶ **Structure**
· Sage-N-Scribe

▶ **Materials**
· Transparency 1.2.3
· 1 sheet of paper and pencil per pair of students

Graphic

Setup:
In pairs, Student A is the Sage; Student B is the Scribe. Students fold a sheet of paper in half and each writes his/her name on one half.

1. The Sage gives the Scribe step-by-step instructions on how to graph problem one on a number line.

2. The Scribe records the Sage's solution step-by-step in writing on the Sage's side of the paper.

3. If the Sage is correct, the Scribe praises the Sage. Otherwise, the Scribe coaches, then praises.

4. Students switch roles for the next problem.

ACTIVITY 5
FACTORS OR TERMS?

▶ **Structure**
· RallyRobin

▶ **Materials**
· Transparency 1.2.4

Algebraic

1. Teacher poses multiple problems using Transparency 1.2.4.

2. In pairs, students take turns orally stating whether the problem is made up of terms or factors.

ACTIVITY

6

REWRITE ME

Algebraic

1. Teacher poses many problems using Transparency 1.2.4.

2. Partner A rewrites the expression in the first problem using coefficients or exponents.

3. Partner B watches, listens, checks, and praises.

4. Partner B rewrites the expression using coefficients or exponents in the next problem.

5. Partner A watches, listens, checks, and praises.

6. Repeat process rotating roles until all problems are complete.

▶ **Structure**
• RallyCoach

▶ **Materials**
• Transparency 1.2.4
• 1 sheet of paper and pencil per pair of students

ACTIVITY

7 **EVALUATE ME**

Algebraic

Setup:
In pairs, Student A is the Sage; Student B is the Scribe. Students fold a sheet of paper in half and each writes his/her name on one half.

1. The Sage gives the Scribe step-by-step instructions on how to evaluate problem one.

2. The Scribe records the Sage's solution step-by-step in writing on the Sage's side of the paper.

3. If the Sage is correct, the Scribe praises the Sage. Otherwise, the Scribe coaches, then praises.

4. Students switch roles for the next problem.

▶ **Structure**
• Sage-N-Scribe

▶ **Materials**
• Transparency 1.2.5
• 1 sheet of paper and pencil per pair of students

ACTIVITY

8 EVALUATE ME SIMULTANEOUSLY

▶ **Structure**
• Simultaneous RoundTable

▶ **Materials**
• Transparency 1.2.6
• 1 sheet of paper and pencil per student

Algebraic

Setup:
Teammate 1 writes problem one at the top of his/her paper and the values of each variable. Teammate 2 writes problem two at the top of his/her paper and the values of each variable. Teammate 3 writes problem three at the top of his/her paper and the values of each variable. Teammate 4 writes problem four at the top of his/her paper and the values of each variable.

Round One
1. All four students respond simultaneously by substituting the numbers for the appropriate variables into the problems found at the top of their paper and initialing his/her work.

2. Students signal they are done by turning over their paper so they can work at their own pace.

3. Students pass papers one person clockwise. Each teammate checks to see if the numbers were substituted correctly on the paper he/she received, coaching the teammate who did the work if it is incorrect. Then all four students respond simultaneously by performing the first operation that should be done, based on the order of operations the students learned in lesson 1, and initialing his/her work.

4. Students signal they are done by turning over their paper so they can work at their own pace.

5. Students pass their papers one person clockwise. Each teammate checks the work on the paper he/she received, coaching the teammate who did the work if it is incorrect. Then all four students respond

simultaneously by performing the next operation and initialing his/her work.

6. Students signal they are done by turning over their paper so they can work at their own pace.

7. Students pass their papers one person clockwise. Each teammate checks the work on the paper he/she received, coaching the teammate who did the problem if it is incorrect. Then all four students respond simultaneously by performing the final operation and initialing his/her work.

8. Students signal they are done by turning over their paper so they can work at their own pace.

9. Students pass their papers one person clockwise. Each teammate checks the work on the paper he/she received, coaching the teammate who did the work if it is incorrect.

ACTIVITY

9 WRITE ME IN SYMBOLS

▶ **Structure**
• RallyCoach

▶ **Materials**
• Transparency 1.2.7
• 1 sheet of paper and pencil per pair of students

Algebraic

1. Teacher poses many problems using Transparency 1.2.7.

2. Partner A rewrites the expression in the first problem using symbols.

3. Partner B watches, listens, checks, and praises.

4. Partner B rewrites the expression using symbols in the next problem.

5. Partner A watches, listens, checks, and praises.

6. Repeat process rotating roles until all problems are complete.

Cooperative Learning and Pre-Algebra: Becky Bride
Kagan Publishing • 1 (800) 933-2667 • www.KaganOnline.com

ACTIVITY

10 SIMPLIFY MY EXPRESSION

Algebraic

Setup:
In pairs, Student A is the Sage; Student B is the Scribe. Students fold a sheet of paper in half and each writes his/her name on one half.

1. The Sage gives the Scribe step-by-step instructions on how to simplify problem one.

2. The Scribe records the Sage's solution step-by-step in writing on the Sage's side of the paper.

3. If the Sage is correct, the Scribe praises the Sage. Otherwise, the Scribe coaches, then praises.

4. Students switch roles for the next problem.

▶ **Structure**
• Sage-N-Scribe

▶ **Materials**
• Transparency 1.2.8
• 1 sheet of paper and pencil per pair of students

ACTIVITY

11 WRITE AN EXPRESSION FOR MY APPLICATION

Algebraic

1. Teacher poses many problems using Transparency 1.2.9.

2. Partner A writes an expression for problem one.

3. Partner B watches, listens, checks, and praises.

4. Partner B writes an expression for the next problem.

5. Partner A watches, listens, checks, and praises.

6. Repeat process rotating roles until all problems are complete.

▶ **Structure**
• RallyCoach

▶ **Materials**
• Transparency 1.2.9
• 1 sheet of paper and pencil per pair of students

ACTIVITY

12 APPLYING EXPRESSIONS IN GEOMETRY

▶ **Structure**
· Sage-N-Scribe

▶ **Materials**
· Blacklines 1.2.10 and 1.2.11
· 1 sheet of paper and pencil per pair of students
· 1 formula sheet per pair of students

Algebraic

Setup:
In pairs, Student A is the Sage; Student B is the Scribe. Students fold a sheet of paper in half and each writes his/her name on one half.

1. The Sage gives the Scribe step-by-step instructions on how to evaluate problem one.

2. The Scribe records the Sage's solution step-by-step in writing on the Sage's side of the paper.

3. If the Sage is correct, the Scribe praises the Sage. Otherwise, the Scribe coaches, then praises.

4. Students switch roles for the next problem.

ACTIVITY

13 WHAT DID WE LEARN?

▶ **Structure**
· RoundTable Consensus

▶ **Materials**
· 1 large sheet of paper per team
· 1 different colored pen or pencil for each student in the team

Synthesis

1. Each teammate signs his/her name in the upper right corner of the team paper with the colored pen/pencil he/she is using.

2. One teammate writes *"Expression"* in the center of the team paper in a rectangle.

3. Teammate 1 shares with the team one core concept he/she learned in the unit.

4. The student checks for consensus.

5. The teammates show agreement or lack of agreement with thumbs up or down.

6. If there is agreement, the students celebrate and the teammate records the core concept on the graphic organizer, connecting it with a line to the main idea, *Whole Number Expressions.* If not, teammates discuss the response until there is agreement and then they celebrate.

7. Play continues with the next student's core concept, until all core concepts are exhausted.

8. Repeat steps 3–7 with teammates adding details to each core concept and making bridges between related ideas.

Cooperative Learning and Pre-Algebra: Becky Bride
Kagan Publishing • 1 (800) 933-2667 • www.KaganOnline.com

1&2 READ ME TWO WAYS
GIVE AN EXAMPLE

Structure: RallyRobin

Activity 1: Read each inequality from the left, then from the right. For the last four, read from the center.

Activity 2: Give a number that makes the statement true.

1. $x > 4$

2. $y \leq 5$

3. $8 \leq m$

4. $9 > p$

5. $q < 10$

6. $16 \leq h$

7. $4 < d \leq 20$

8. $42 \geq x \geq 10$

9. $31 \geq n \geq 5$

10. $12 < t < 63$

Answers will vary.

ACTIVITY
3

WHERE DO I BELONG?

Structure: RoundRobin

Taking turns, place each of your cards on the inequality that it fits.

$$x < 8$$

$$8 \leq x \leq 19$$

$$x \geq 32$$

$$19 < x < 32$$

Cooperative Learning and Pre-Algebra: Becky Bride
Kagan Publishing • 1 (800) 933-2667 • www.KaganOnline.com

4 GRAPH MY INEQUALITY

Structure: Sage-N-Scribe

Graph each problem on a different number line.

1. $x > 5$

2. $h \leq 10$

3. $18 > x \geq 15$

4. $q \geq 18$

5. $11 \leq p < 12$

6. $14 > y > 8$

Answers will vary.

ACTIVITIES 5&6 FACTORS OR TERMS? REWRITE ME

Structure: RallyRobin (Activity 5)
Structure: RallyCoach (Activity 6)

Directions:

Activity 5: State whether the expression is made of factors or terms.

Activity 6: Rewrite each problem using coefficients or exponents.

1. $x + x + x$

2. $p \times p \times p \times p$

3. $h \times h$

4. $m + m + m + m + m$

5. $y \times y \times y \times y \times y \times y$

6. $d + d + d + d + d + d$

Answers:
Activity 5

1. terms	2. factors	3. factors
4. terms	5. factors	6. terms

Activity 6

1. $3x$	2. p^4	3. h^2
4. $5m$	5. y^6	6. $6d$

Cooperative Learning and Pre-Algebra: Becky Bride
Kagan Publishing • 1 (800) 933-2667 • www.KaganOnline.com

Structure: Sage-N-Scribe

Evaluate each of the following if $x = 12$, $y = 3$, $p = 2$, $m = 6$, and $n = 1$.

1. $2x + y$

2. $y^2 - p$

3. $3p^2 - (m + n)$

4. $4x - 5p$

5. $\dfrac{x}{y + n}$

6. $\dfrac{xy}{p^2} + n$

7. $5y^2 - \dfrac{m}{p}$

8. $6(3 + y^2) - 4m$

Answers:

1. 27	2. 7	3. 5	4. 38
5. 3	6. 10	7. 42	8. 48

EVALUATE ME SIMULTANEOUSLY

Structure: Simultaneous RoundTable

Listen to the teacher for instructions.
$x = 60 \qquad y = 4 \qquad p = 3$

1. $\dfrac{x}{2p} + y$

2. $4(y + p)^2$

3. $5p + y^2$

4. $\left(\dfrac{x}{y}\right)^2 + p$

Answers:
1. 14   2. 196   3. 31   4. 228

Cooperative Learning and Pre-Algebra: Becky Bride
Kagan Publishing • 1 (800) 933-2667 • www.KaganOnline.com

WRITE ME IN SYMBOLS

Structure: RallyCoach

Rewrite each of the following using symbols.

1. Four increased by some number

2. Some number divided by nine

3. The sum of twelve and some number

4. Four times some number increased by three

5. Some number divided by three decreased by eight

6. Six times the difference of some number and one

7. Some number subtracted from ten

8. The product of some number and 3 increased by 2

Answers:
1. $4 + x$ 2. $y \div 9$ 3. $12 + m$ 4. $4x + 3$
5. $h \div 3 - 8$ 6. $6(y - 1)$ 7. $10 - w$ 8. $3f + 2$

ACTIVITY

10 SIMPLIFY MY EXPRESSION

Structure: Sage-N-Scribe

Simplify each expression.

1. $5m + 2 - 3m$

2. $4 - 7h + 11$

3. $7x^2 + 2x - x + 2x^2$

4. $g - g^2 + 8g - 1$

5. $10w + 7wy - 3w$

6. $7k + k^2 - k + 3k^2$

7. $d^2 + 9d + 4d^2 - d$

8. $9n + 2np + 8np$

Answers:

1. $2m + 2$ 2. $15 - 7h$ 3. $9x^2 + x$ 4. $9g - g^2 - 1$
5. $7w + 7wy$ 6. $6k + 4k^2$ 7. $5d^2 + 8d$ 8. $9n + 10np$

Cooperative Learning and Pre-Algebra: Becky Bride
Kagan Publishing • 1 (800) 933-2667 • www.KaganOnline.com

WRITE AN EXPRESSION FOR MY APPLICATION

Structure: RallyCoach

Write each problem as an expression.

1. Five friends share *x* cookies equally.

2. The amount of money Sue has left from a twenty-dollar bill after she buys a CD for *d* dollars.

3. The cost of a fifteen-dollar shirt and two pairs of pants whose price is *p* dollars each.

4. The cost of nine candy bars if the price of each is *b* dollars.

5. The total number of tickets sold at the volleyball game if forty student tickets were sold and *m* number of adult tickets are sold.

6. The amount of money made at a bake sale if *c* cookies were sold for one dollar each and if *b* brownies were sold for two dollars each.

Answers:

1. $x \div 5$	2. $20 - d$	3. $15 + 2p$
4. $9b$	5. $40 + m$	6. $c + 2b$

Blackline 1.2.10

ACTIVITY 12 APPLYING EXPRESSIONS IN GEOMETRY

Structure: Sage-N-Scribe

Evaluate each of the following showing work.

1. The top of a rectangular desk has a width of 24 inches and a length of 30 inches. What is the area of the top of the desk?

2. A triangular sail has a base measurement of 8 feet and a height of 14 feet. How many square feet of canvas is needed to make the sail?

3. A rectangular suitcase has dimensions 15 inches wide, 30 inches long, and 9 inches deep. What is the volume of the suitcase?

4. A porch needs to be painted and is in the shape of a trapezoid. If one base is 4 meters long, the other base is 5 meters long, and the height is 4 meters, how many square meters will be painted?

5. A flag is in the shape of a rhombus. If one diagonal measures 44 centimeters and the other diagonal measures 38 centimeters, what is the area of the flag?

6. Kim has a flower garden in the shape of a square with one side of the garden bordering Kim's house. How many feet of fencing is required to fence the garden if a side of the garden is 16 feet?

7. Find the sum of the angles of a polygon that has 12 sides.

8. Find the measure of each angle of an equiangular polygon with 8 sides.

Answers:
1. 720 in.²   2. 56 ft²   3. 4,050 in.³   4. 18 m²
5. 836 cm²   6. 48 ft   7. 1,800 degrees   8. 135 degrees

Cooperative Learning and Pre-Algebra: Becky Bride
Kagan Publishing • 1 (800) 933-2667 • www.KaganOnline.com

ACTIVITY 12 MATHEMATICAL FORMULA REFERENCE SHEET

Area

rectangle: $A = l \times w$

triangle: $A = \dfrac{b \times h}{2}$

trapezoid: $A = \dfrac{h(b_1 + b_2)}{2}$

square: $A = s^2$

rhombus: $A = \dfrac{(d_1 \times d_2)}{2}$

circle: $A = \pi r^2$

Surface Area

sphere: $A = 4\pi r^2$

rectangular box: $A = 2(lh + wh + wl)$

cylinder: $A = 2\pi r^2 + 2\pi rh$

cone: $A = \pi r^2 + 2\pi rl$

Volume

sphere: $V = \dfrac{3}{4}\pi r^3$

rectangular box: $V = l \times w \times h$

cylinder: $V = \pi r^2 H$

cone: $V = \dfrac{1}{3}\pi r^2 H$

Perimeter: sum of the sides of a figure

Circumference of a circle: $C = \pi d$

In a polygon, the sum of the measures of the interior angles is equal to $180(n - 2)$.

In a polygon with all equal angles, the measure of an interior angle is equal to $\dfrac{180(n - 2)}{n}$

Key

b = base of a 2-d figure
h = height of a 2-d figure
l = length
w = width
L = slant height
SA = surface area
d = diameter
r = radius
A = area of a 2-d figure
C = circumference
V = volume
H = height of 3-d figure
n = the number of sides
    in a polygon

LESSON 3
EQUATIONS

This lesson introduces students to the concepts of solving one- and two-step equations. Activity 1 is a teacher demonstrated activity that teaches the concept of equation solving. Activities 2–5 have the students analyze each equation. In Activities 6–7, the students will solve equations. Two-step equations are analyzed in activities 8–9 and the remainder of the activities has the students process equation solving using higher levels of thinking.

ACTIVITY 1
GETTING AT THE CONCEPT

This activity is not a student activity but a teacher demonstration. You will use a hammer, screwdriver, nail, screw, and three boards to connect, then disconnect, the boards. Students will learn that in algebra there are tools like hammers and screwdrivers (+, −, x, ÷) that can be used to isolate a variable (the painted board) by performing the inverse operation on both sides of an equation. By first putting the boards together and then taking them apart, the students will see that the last board connected is the first board to be disconnected. This drives home the point that the order of operations for +/− and x/÷ must be done in the reverse order when solving an equation—anything attached to the variable via addition and subtraction must be disconnected before anything attached to the variable via multiplication and division. If you want students to disconnect addition by adding the opposite of the number to both sides of an equation rather than using subtraction, then as you disconnect the boards you can emphasize that the screwdriver must be turned in the opposite direction compared to when you put them together. The opposite end of the hammer is required to disconnect the nail. Once the hammer, screwdriver, nail, screw, and boards are brought out in class you have immediately piqued the students' interest and have their undivided attention.

▶ **Structure**
• Teacher Demonstration

▶ **Materials**
• 3 boards, 1 flat-head screw, and 1 double-headed nail (preferably predrilled for easy use)
• 1 hammer
• 1 screwdriver

Making the Manipulative
The manipulative you need can be easily made. A good length for the three boards is 9–12 inches and any width 1.5 inches or more is fine. The depth of the boards can become an issue if you don't want the nail to protrude from the bottom board. A depth of 1.5 inches is ideal. Paint one of the boards any color you choose. This board will ultimately be the variable and will be the bottom board when they are all assembled. Place a non-painted board on top of the painted board, and secure these with a counter sunk flat-head screw. A flat-head screw is crucial because another board will be placed on top of this board and needs a flat surface. Place the final non-painted board on top of the other non-painted board and secure these with the nail (make sure the board covers the top of the screw). Disassemble these pieces before starting the activity.

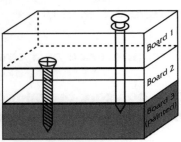

First Concept to be Established
Whatever you do to one side of the equation, you must do to the other side.

Notice the operative word here is **established**. You will lead the students to this concept, and they will have it before you are finished with all the examples. The basic format to achieve this is the following:

64

Chapter 1: Whole Numbers
Lesson Three

Cooperative Learning and Pre-Algebra: Becky Bride
Kagan Publishing • 1 (800) 933-2667 • www.KaganOnline.com

1) Write an equation on the board such as 5 = 5.

2) Perform an operation to only one side of the equation and ask if the result is still equal. Performing the operations vertically works best because the students can easily see what was done. 5 = 5 would now look like

$$5 = 5$$
$$\underline{+3}$$
$$8 = 5$$

The students instantly see that the equation is no longer equal.

3) Ask the students what can be done to fix it so it is equal again without changing the left side. The response will instantly be to add 3 to the other side.

4) Repeat steps 1–3 with a new equation and a new operation each time—sometimes performing the operation on the left of the equation and sometimes performing the operation on the right side of the equation. Use subtraction, multiplication, division, squaring, and square rooting.

5) Tell the students that you are trying to make a point. Ask them what that point may be.

The Demonstration
1. Begin with the three boards apart. Explain that you need to put the three boards together. The **tools** you have are a hammer and a screwdriver, and the **connectors** are a nail and a screw.

2. Pick up the painted board and another board and explain that you want to connect them with the screw. Pick up the

hammer to connect the boards with the screw. Someone in the class should tell you that your tool is wrong. Ask them how they know it is the wrong tool. Emphasize that the **connector** then determined the **tool** that was used.

3. Join the third board to the other two boards. Pick up the nail and the screwdriver. Someone will tell you that the screwdriver is the wrong tool. Ask the class why you can't use the screwdriver—that it worked well the first time. Ask again how they knew it was the wrong tool. Emphasize again that the **connector** determined the **tool** that was used.

4. Now the process begins to separate the boards. This is what you wanted to do from the beginning, but they had to be put together before you could take them apart. Emphasize that the **goal is to get the painted board by itself**. To do this, pick up the screwdriver. Someone will mention that it is the wrong tool. The logical question is "But I used it first when I put the boards together. Why can't I use it first again?" You will have yet another opportunity to emphasize that the **connector** determines the **tool**. As you begin to take out the nail, use the same end of the hammer that you put the nail in with. The goal is to get someone to tell you that you need to use the **opposite** end. Remove the nail to disconnect the top board.

5. There are two boards still connected. Re-iterate that the goal is to get the painted board by itself and try to use the hammer to remove the

screw. By now there should be many students telling you that the tool is wrong. This is yet another opportunity to emphasize that the **connector** determines which **tool** is required. When using the screwdriver, turn it the wrong way since that was how you used it when you connected the boards. Someone will tell you to turn it in the **opposite** direction. Capitalize on the concept of **opposite**. Remove the screw to disconnect the middle board.

6. The boards are now apart. Emphasize one more time that the goal—getting the painted board by itself—was met.

Making the Connection
Ask the students what this demonstration had to do with math and they will quickly tell you "absolutely nothing." That is when you can tell them that it has everything to do with math. The painted board represents the variable in an equation. The goal of equation solving is to get the variable by itself on one side of the equation. In order to do that, the students must decide which numbers are **connected** to the variable, how they are connected, and what **tool** (+, −, x or ÷) they will use to disconnect the numbers from the variable. During the disconnect stage, whatever is done to one side of an equation must be done to the other side of the equation. Modeling one-step equations—emphasizing which number is connected to the variable, how it is connected, and which tool is necessary to disconnect the number from the variable—solidifies the lesson.

ACTIVITY

2 IS THE VARIABLE ALONE?

▶ **Structure**
· RallyRobin

▶ **Materials**
· Transparency 1.3.1

Algebraic

1. Teacher poses multiple problems using Transparency 1.3.1.

2. In pairs, students take turns orally stating whether the variable is alone in each problem.

ACTIVITY

3 WHO IS ATTACHED?

▶ **Structure**
· RallyRobin

▶ **Materials**
· Transparency 1.3.1

Algebraic

1. Teacher poses multiple problems using Transparency 1.3.1.

2. In pairs, students take turns orally stating who is attached to the variable in each problem.

ACTIVITY

4 NAME THE CONNECTING OPERATION

▶ **Structure**
· RallyRobin

▶ **Materials**
· Transparency 1.3.1

Algebraic

1. Teacher poses multiple problems using Transparency 1.3.1.

2. In pairs, students take turns orally naming the connecting operation in each problem.

ACTIVITY

5 NAME THE DISCONNECTING OPERATION

▶ **Structure**
· RallyRobin

▶ **Materials**
· Transparency 1.3.1

Algebraic

1. Teacher poses multiple problems using Transparency 1.3.1.

2. In pairs, students take turns orally naming the disconnecting operation in each problem.

Chapter 1: Whole Numbers
Lesson Three

Cooperative Learning and Pre-Algebra: Becky Bride
Kagan Publishing • 1 (800) 933-2667 • www.KaganOnline.com

ACTIVITY

6 SOLVE ME

Algebraic

Setup:
In pairs, Student A is the Sage; Student B is the Scribe. Students fold a sheet of paper in half and each writes his/her name on one half.

1. The Sage gives the Scribe step-by-step instructions on how to solve problem one.

2. The Scribe records the Sage's solution step-by-step in writing on the Sage's side of the paper.

3. If the Sage is correct, the Scribe praises the Sage. Otherwise, the Scribe coaches, then praises.

4. Students switch roles for the next problem.

▶ **Structure**
· Sage-N-Scribe

▶ **Materials**
· Transparency 1.3.1
· 1 sheet of paper and pencil per pair of students

ACTIVITY

7 SOLVE AGAIN

Algebraic

Setup:
In pairs, Student A is the Sage; Student B is the Scribe. Students fold a sheet of paper in half and each writes his/her name on one half.

1. The Sage gives the Scribe step-by-step instructions on how to solve problem one.

2. The Scribe records the Sage's solution step-by-step in writing on the Sage's side of the paper.

3. If the Sage is correct, the Scribe praises the Sage. Otherwise, the Scribe coaches, then praises.

4. Students switch roles for the next problem

▶ **Structure**
· Sage-N-Scribe

▶ **Materials**
· Transparency 1.3.2
· 1 sheet of paper and pencil per pair of students

ACTIVITY

8 WHO IS CONNECTED AND HOW?

Algebraic

1. Teacher poses multiple problems using Transparency 1.3.3.

2. In pairs, students take turns orally stating "who" is connected to each variable and how it is connected in each problem.

▶ **Structure**
· RallyRobin

▶ **Materials**
· Transparency 1.3.3

ACTIVITY

9 WHO GETS DISCONNECTED FIRST?

▶ **Structure**
· RallyRobin

▶ **Materials**
· Transparency 1.3.3

Algebraic

1. Teacher poses multiple problems using Transparency 1.3.3.

2. In pairs, students take turns orally stating "who" gets disconnected first and what operation will be used to disconnect it for each problem.

ACTIVITY

10 SOLVE ME—TAKE 2

▶ **Structure**
· Sage-N-Scribe

▶ **Materials**
· Transparency 1.3.3
· 1 sheet of paper and pencil per pair of students

Algebraic

Setup:
In pairs, Student A is the Sage; Student B is the Scribe. Students fold a sheet of paper in half and each writes his/her name on one half.

1. The Sage gives the Scribe step-by-step instructions on how to solve problem one.

2. The Scribe records the Sage's solution step-by-step in writing on the Sage's side of the paper.

3. If the Sage is correct, the Scribe praises the Sage. Otherwise, the Scribe coaches, then praises.

4. Students switch roles for the next problem.

ACTIVITY

11 PUTTING IT ALL TOGETHER

▶ **Structure**
· Sage-N-Scribe

▶ **Materials**
· Transparency 1.3.4
· 1 sheet of paper and pencil per pair of students

Algebraic

Setup:
In pairs, Student A is the Sage; Student B is the Scribe. Students fold a sheet of paper in half and each writes his/her name on one half.

1. The Sage gives the Scribe step-by-step instructions on how to solve problem one.

2. The Scribe records the Sage's solution step-by-step in writing on the Sage's side of the paper.

3. If the Sage is correct, the Scribe praises the Sage. Otherwise, the Scribe coaches, then praises.

4. Students switch roles for the next problem.

Chapter 1: Whole Numbers
Lesson Three

Cooperative Learning and Pre-Algebra: Becky Bride
Kagan Publishing • 1 (800) 933-2667 • www.KaganOnline.com

WHOLE NUMBERS

{0,1}

ACTIVITY

12 FIND MY MISTAKES

Algebraic

1. Teacher poses many problems using Transparency 1.3.5.

2. Partner A finds the mistakes in problem one, describing them on the paper.

3. Partner B watches, listens, checks, and praises.

4. Partner B finds the mistakes and describes them on paper for the next problem.

5. Partner A watches, listens, checks, and praises.

6. Repeat for remaining problems starting at step 2.

▶ **Structure**
• RallyCoach

▶ **Materials**
• Transparency 1.3.5
• 1 sheet of paper and pencil per pair of students

ACTIVITY

13 APPLYING EQUATIONS

Algebraic

Setup:
In pairs, Student A is the Sage; Student B is the Scribe. Students fold a sheet of paper in half and each writes his/her name on one half.

1. The Sage gives the Scribe step-by-step instructions on how to solve problem one.

2. The Scribe records the Sage's solution step-by-step in writing on the Sage's side of the paper.

3. If the Sage is correct, the Scribe praises the Sage. Otherwise, the Scribe coaches, then praises.

4. Students switch roles for the next problem.

▶ **Structure**
• Sage-N-Scribe

▶ **Materials**
• Blackline 1.3.6
• 1 sheet of paper and pencil per pair of student

ACTIVITY

14 WHAT DID WE LEARN?

▶ **Structure**
· RoundTable Consensus

▶ **Materials**
· 1 large sheet of paper per team
· 1 different colored pen or pencil for each student in the team

Synthesis

1. Each teammate signs his/her name in the upper right corner of the team paper with the colored pen/pencil he/she is using.

2. One teammate writes *"Equations"* in the center of the team paper in a rectangle.

3. Teammate 1 shares with the team one core concept he/she learned in the unit.

4. The student checks for consensus.

5. The teammates show agreement or lack of agreement with thumbs up or down.

6. If there is agreement, the students celebrate and the teammate records the core concept on the graphic organizer, connecting it with a line to the main idea—*Whole Number Equations.* If not, teammates discuss the response until there is agreement and then they celebrate.

7. Play continues with the next student's core concept, until all core concepts are exhausted.

8. Repeat steps 3–7 with teammates adding details to each core concept and making bridges between related ideas.

Cooperative Learning and Pre-Algebra: Becky Bride
Kagan Publishing • 1 (800) 933-2667 • www.KaganOnline.com

IS THE VARIABLE ALONE?
WHO IS ATTACHED?
NAME THE CONNECTING OPERATION
NAME THE DISCONNECTING OPERATION
SOLVE ME

Structure: Rally Robin (Activities 2–5)
Structure: Sage-N-Scribe (Activity 6)

1. $12 = p - 15$

2. $6 + h = 32$

3. $\dfrac{w}{8} = 16$

4. $15(5) = g$

5. $24 = 6k$

6. $16 = \dfrac{f}{4}$

7. $2 + 9 = e$

8. $x - 13 = 22$

Answers:
Activity 6

1. 27	2. 26	3. 128	4. 75
5. 4	6. 64	7. 11	8. 35

7 SOLVE AGAIN

Structure: Sage-N-Scribe

Solve each equation.

1. $\dfrac{d}{3} = 12$

2. $45 = 12 + e$

3. $72 = x - 43$

4. $\dfrac{v}{7} = 11$

5. $18 + h = 33$

6. $108 = 6k$

7. $n \times 8 = 128$

8. $z - 47 = 62$

Answers:
1. 36   2. 33   3. 115   4. 77
5. 15   6. 18   7. 16   8. 109

Cooperative Learning and Pre-Algebra: Becky Bride
Kagan Publishing • 1 (800) 933-2667 • www.KaganOnline.com

ACTIVITIES

WHO IS CONNECTED AND HOW?
WHO GETS CONNECTED FIRST?
SOLVE ME—TAKE 2

Structure: RallyRobin (Activity 8)
Structure: RallyRobin (Activity 9)
Structure: Sage-N-Scribe (Activity 10)

1. $2w - 9 = 19$ 2. $\dfrac{v}{7} + 5 = 8$

3. $9 + \dfrac{u}{6} = 39$ 4. $19 = 6k - 23$

5. $52 = 5k - 13$ 6. $26 = \dfrac{f}{4} + 20$

7. $6 = 2 + \dfrac{f}{3}$ 8. $15 = 7 + 2k$

Answers:

1. 14	2. 21	3. 180	4. 7
5. 13	6. 24	7. 12	8. 4

PUTTING IT ALL TOGETHER

Structure: Sage-N-Scribe

Solve each equation.

1. $2 = w - 9$

2. $n = 8 + 124$

3. $3 + \dfrac{u}{6} = 12$

4. $12 = 8 + 2c$

5. $17 = 11 + 3e$

6. $12h = 60$

7. $v = 2 + \dfrac{15}{3}$

8. $3 + \dfrac{u}{8} = 5$

Answers:

1. 11	2. 132	3. 54	4. 2
5. 2	6. 5	7. 7	8. 16

Cooperative Learning and Pre-Algebra: Becky Bride
Kagan Publishing • 1 (800) 933-2667 • www.KaganOnline.com

ACTIVITY

12 FIND MY MISTAKES

Structure: RallyCoach

Find and describe the mistakes made in the problems below.

1. $4p - 2 = 16$
$\dfrac{4p - 2}{4} = \dfrac{16}{4}$
$p - 2 = 4$
$\underline{+\ 2\quad +2}$
$p = 6$

2. $49 = 2w - 9$
$\underline{-9\qquad -\ 9}$
$40 = 2w$
$\dfrac{40}{2} = \dfrac{2w}{2}$
$20 = w$

3. $10 = 18 + 2k$
$\underline{-10\ -10}$
$0 = 2k$
$\dfrac{0}{2} = \dfrac{2k}{2}$
$0 = k$

4. $17 = 3d - 11$
$\underline{-11 = \qquad -\ 11}$
$\dfrac{6}{3} = \dfrac{3d}{3}$
$3 = d$

5. $3 + 4m = 17$
$\underline{-3 - 3}$
$m = 17$

6. $\dfrac{u}{3} - 7 = 25$
$\underline{\times 3\quad \times 3}$
$u - 21 = 25$
$\underline{-\ 21\ -\ 21}$
$u = 4$

ACTIVITY
13 **APPLYING EQUATIONS**

Structure: Sage-N-Scribe

Write an equation for each of the following and solve.

1. Yunnia buys 4 pencils that cost p dollars per pencil. She also bought 2 erasers that were one dollar each. If Yunnia spent $10, how much did each pencil cost?

2. Amber is babysitting 4 children. She found 14 cookies and ate two of them. If each child gets c cookies, how many cookies did each child get?

3. Jose's math and English assignment will take the same amount of time to complete. If the history assignment takes 45 minutes and it took Jose 115 minutes to complete his homework, how long did it take to do the math assignment?

4. It takes Will 5 minutes to ride a mile. If Will rode his bike for 90 minutes, How many miles did he ride?

5. Twice some number increased by three is nine. Find the number.

6. Some number divided by six then decreased by seven is 1. Find the number.

7. Ruzlan bought 6 student tickets for five dollars each and 3 adult tickets for y dollars each. If Ruzlan spent $57, how many adult tickets did he buy?

8. Shayla ate 3 candy bars and 3 of her friends ate w candy bars. If there were fifteen candy bars, how many candy bars did her friends eat if each friend ate an equal amount?

Answers:

1. $4p + 2 = 10$; $2   2. $c = \dfrac{14 - 2}{4}$; 3 cookies   3. $2x + 45 = 115$; 35 minutes   4. $5x = 90$: 18 miles

5. $2x + 3 = 9$; 3   6. $\dfrac{n}{6} - 7 = 1$; 48   7. $30 + 3y = 57$; 9 adult tickets   8. $3 + 3w = 15$; 4 bars

Cooperative Learning and Pre-Algebra: Becky Bride
Kagan Publishing • 1 (800) 933-2667 • www.KaganOnline.com

INTEGERS

This chapter begins to spiral the concepts that began in Chapter 1. Integers are placed before fractions and decimals so that these concepts are reinforced in the fraction and decimal chapters. Success at the Algebra 1 level is dependent to a large degree on the ability of students to fluently work with operations on integers. This also gives students the opportunity to work with positive and negative fractions and decimals making these units a little bit different from the typical fraction and decimal units the students have had in the past. Lesson 1 has students work with integers on a arithmetic and graphical level. Lessons 2 and 3 have students work with integers on an algebraic level through expressions and equations. **Introducing the four operations on integers is best done on a concrete level using algebra tiles.** Exploratory investigations using algebra tiles can be found in the book *Cooperative Learning and Algebra 1.* To avoid duplication, the investigations are not included in this book.

LESSON 1 NUMBER SENSE

ACTIVITY 1: Can You Define Me?
ACTIVITY 2: Classify Me
ACTIVITY 3: How Many Ways Can You Graph Me?
ACTIVITY 4: Compare Me
ACTIVITY 5: Plot My Point
ACTIVITY 6: How Many Ordered Pairs Can You Name?
ACTIVITY 7: Add Me
ACTIVITY 8: Subtract Me
ACTIVITY 9: Multiply Me
ACTIVITY 10: Divide Me
ACTIVITY 11: Mix It Up
ACTIVITY 12: All Together
ACTIVITY 13: Expand Me
ACTIVITY 14: Rewrite Using Exponents
ACTIVITY 15: Order of Operations
ACTIVITY 16: What Did We Learn?

LESSON 2 EXPRESSIONS

ACTIVITY 1: Expand My Variable Expression
ACTIVITY 2: Rewrite My Variable Expression Using Exponents
ACTIVITY 3: Graph Me on the Number Line
ACTIVITY 4: Where Do You Belong?
ACTIVITY 5: Evaluate Me
ACTIVITY 6: Simplify My Expression
ACTIVITY 7: Simplify My Expression—Take 2
ACTIVITY 8: What Did We Learn?

LESSON 3 EQUATIONS AND INEQUALITIES

ACTIVITY 1: Solve My Equation
ACTIVITY 2: Can You Solve Me?
ACTIVITY 3: Does My Sign Need to Flip?
ACTIVITY 4: Solve My One-Step Inequality
ACTIVITY 5: Solve My Two-Step Inequality
ACTIVITY 6: Find My Mistakes
ACTIVITY 7: What Did We Learn?

LESSON 1
NUMBER SENSE

This lesson begins with introducing integers as a new set of numbers in the real number system. Activity 2 has students classify numbers that belong to the natural, whole, integer, and/or real number sets, thus reinforcing the sets studied in Chapter 1. Students will compare integers. Integers are graphed on both a number line and coordinate plane. The coordinate plane is expanded from quadrant ± in chapter 1 to all four quadrants. Activities 7–12 have students practice addition, subtraction, multiplication, and division with integers. **Concrete development using algebra tiles is strongly recommended** before doing these activities. Exploratory activities can be found in *Cooperative Learning and Algebra 1*. Students have a difficult time grasping the difference between -4^2 and $(-4)^2$. Students in calculus classes still miss problems because of this concept. Activities 13 and 14 are included to help students understand the difference between these two notations. Activity 15 requires students to use their understanding from Activities 13 and 14 to perform the order of operations. This lesson ends with applications and an activity to synthesize the lesson.

ACTIVITY
1 CAN YOU DEFINE ME?

▶ **Structure**
•Solo-Pair Consensus-Team Consensus

▶ **Materials**
•Blackline 2.1.1 per student
• 1 sheet of paper and pencil per student

Exploratory

Solo
1. Individually, each student completes the exploration.

Pair Consensus
2. For each problem on the investigation, each student shares with his/her partner, using RallyRobin, his/her response. They discuss the problems that they disagree on, trying to come to consensus on the correct response. They mark the problems they can't reach consensus on so

they can focus on them during the team phase. Encourage the students to add to their responses if their partner verbalizes an understanding they did not see.

Team Consensus
3. Each pair shares their responses, using RallyRobin, with the other pair in their team, augmenting their responses if necessary. When the teams are through sharing, each student should have a detailed, complete summary.

Chapter 2: Integers
Lesson One

78

ACTIVITY 2

CLASSIFY ME

Numeric

1. Teacher poses many problems using Transparency 2.1.2.

2. Partner A classifies the number in problem one as a natural, whole, integer, and/or real number writing his/her response on the paper.

3. Partner B watches, listens, checks, and praises.

4. Partner B classifies the number in the next problem.

5. Partner A watches, listens, checks, and praises.

6. Repeat for remaining problems starting at step 2.

▶ **Structure**
• RallyCoach

▶ **Materials**
• Transparency 2.1.2
• 1 sheet of paper and pencil per pair of students

ACTIVITY 3

HOW MANY WAYS CAN YOU GRAPH ME?

Graphic

The purpose of this activity is to have students graph the same number using different scales. This reinforces a similar activity in Chapter 1.

1. Teacher poses many problems using Transparency 2.1.3.

2. Partner A graphs the number in the first problem on a number line, using any scale he/she chooses.

3. Partner B watches, listens, checks, and praises.

4. Partner B graphs the number on a different number line using a different scale of his/her choice.

5. Partner A watches, listens, checks, and praises.

6. Repeat until three graphs are graphed for problem one.

7. Repeat for remaining problems starting at step 2.

▶ **Structure**
• RallyCoach

▶ **Materials**
• Transparency 2.1.3
• 1 sheet of paper, pencil, and ruler per pair of students

Chapter 2: Integers
Lesson One

Cooperative Learning and Pre-Algebra: Becky Bride
Kagan Publishing • 1 (800) 933-2667 • www.KaganOnline.com

ACTIVITY 4

COMPARE ME

▶ **Structure**
• RallyCoach

▶ **Materials**
• Transparency 2.1.4
• 1 sheet of paper and pencil per pair of students

In addition to writing a correct mathematical inequality, this activity also asks the students to write two sentences—one reading the expression from left to right, then the other one reading the expression from right to left.

Numeric

1. Teacher poses many problems using Transparency 2.1.4.

2. Partner A compares the two numbers and writes the problem inserting the correct inequality symbol. Then he/she writes the expression as a

sentence as the inequality would be read from left to right. He/she writes a second sentence as the inequality would be read from right to left.

3. Partner B watches, listens, checks, and praises.

4. Partner B repeats step 2 for the next problem.

5. Partner A watches, listens, checks, and praises.

6. Repeat for remaining problems starting at step 2.

ACTIVITY 5

PLOT MY POINT

▶ **Structure**
• RallyCoach

▶ **Materials**
• Transparency 2.1.5
• 1 sheet of graph paper and pencil per pair of students.

Graphic

Setup:
Have the students draw a coordinate plane on one side of the graph paper with single increment axes scales. On the other side of the paper, have students draw a coordinate plane with scales on the axes of increment two.

1. Teacher poses many problems using Transparency 2.1.5.

2. Partner A graphs and labels the point in the first problem on the first coordinate plane.

3. Partner B watches, listens, checks, and praises.

4. Partner B graphs and labels the next point on the same coordinate plane.

5. Partner A watches, listens, checks, and praises.

6. Repeat for remaining problems starting at step 2.

7. Repeat entire activity on the reverse side of the paper.

Cooperative Learning and Pre-Algebra: Becky Bride
Kagan Publishing • 1 (800) 933-2667 • www.KaganOnline.com

ACTIVITY

6

HOW MANY ORDERED PAIRS CAN YOU NAME?

Graphic

1. Teacher poses multiple problems using Transparency 2.1.6.

2. In pairs, students take turns writing a list of ordered pairs that fall in the requested quadrant or on the requested axis.

▶ **Structure**
· RallyTable

▶ **Materials**
· Transparency 2.1.6
· 1 sheet of paper and pencil per pair of students

ACTIVITY

7

ADD ME

Numeric

Setup:
In pairs, Student A is the Sage; Student B is the Scribe. Students fold a sheet of paper in half and each writes his/her name on one half.

1. The Sage gives the Scribe step-by-step instructions on how to add the numbers in problem one.

2. The Scribe records the Sage's solution step-by-step in writing on the Sage's side of the paper.

3. If the Sage is correct, the Scribe praises the Sage. Otherwise, the Scribe coaches, then praises.

4. Students switch roles for the next problem.

▶ **Structure**
· Sage-N-Scribe

▶ **Materials**
· Transparency 2.1.7
· 1 sheet of paper and pencil per pair of students

ACTIVITY

8

SUBTRACT ME

Numeric

Setup:
In pairs, Student A is the Sage; Student B is the Scribe. Students fold a sheet of paper in half and each writes his/her name on one half.

1. The Sage gives the Scribe step-by-step instructions on how to subtract the numbers in problem one.

2. The Scribe records the Sage's solution step-by-step in writing on the Sage's side of the paper.

3. If the Sage is correct, the Scribe praises the Sage. Otherwise, the Scribe coaches, then praises.

4. Students switch roles for the next problem.

▶ **Structure**
· Sage-N-Scribe

▶ **Materials**
· Transparency 2.1.8
· 1 sheet of paper and pencil per pair of students

ACTIVITY

9 MULTIPLY ME

▶ **Structure**
• Sage-N-Scribe

▶ **Materials**
• Transparency 2.1.9
• 1 sheet of paper and pencil per pair of students

Numeric

Setup:
In pairs, Student A is the Sage; Student B is the Scribe. Students fold a sheet of paper in half and each writes his/her name on one half.

1. The Sage gives the Scribe step-by-step instructions on how to multiply the numbers in problem one.

2. The Scribe records the Sage's solution step-by-step in writing on the Sage's side of the paper.

3. If the Sage is correct, the Scribe praises the Sage. Otherwise, the Scribe coaches, then praises.

4. Students switch roles for the next problem.

ACTIVITY

10 DIVIDE ME

▶ **Structure**
• Sage-N-Scribe

▶ **Materials**
• Transparency 2.1.10
• 1 sheet of paper and pencil per pair of students

Numeric

Setup:
In pairs, Student A is the Sage; Student B is the Scribe. Students fold a sheet of paper in half and each writes his/her name on one half.

1. The Sage gives the Scribe step-by-step instructions on how to divide the numbers in problem one.

2. The Scribe records the Sage's solution step-by-step in writing on the Sage's side of the paper.

3. If the Sage is correct, the Scribe praises the Sage. Otherwise, the Scribe coaches, then praises.

4. Students switch roles for the next problem.

Cooperative Learning and Pre-Algebra: Becky Bride
Kagan Publishing • 1 (800) 933-2667 • www.KaganOnline.com

ACTIVITY 11 — MIX IT UP

Numeric

Setup:
The cards need to be copied onto cardstock and cut into individual cards. Cards are distributed to the students, 1 card per student.

1. StandUp–HandUp–PairUp.

2. Partner A quizzes his/her partner, asking what the sum of the numbers on their two cards is.

3. Partner B answers.

4. Partner A praises or coaches.

5. Partner B quizzes his/her partner, asking what the difference of the numbers on their two cards is.

6. Partner A answers.

7. Partner B praises or coaches.

8. Partners trade cards.

9. Repeat steps 1–6 as many times as the teacher chooses.

Variations: The operations that the students perform can change, giving students practice on multiply also. Be careful with division because the answer may not be an integer.

▶ **Structure**
• Quiz-Quiz-Trade

▶ **Materials**
• 1 set of Integer Cards Blackline 2.1.11 (1 card per student)
• 1 sheet of paper and pencil per student

ACTIVITY 12 — ALL TOGETHER

Numeric

Setup:
In pairs, Student A is the Sage; Student B is the Scribe. Students fold a sheet of paper in half and each writes his/her name on one half.

1. The Sage gives the Scribe step-by-step instructions on how to solve problem one.

2. The Scribe records the Sage's solution step-by-step in writing on the Sage's side of the paper.

3. If the Sage is correct, the Scribe praises the Sage. Otherwise, the Scribe coaches, then praises.

4. Students switch roles for the next problem.

▶ **Structure**
• Sage-N-Scribe

▶ **Materials**
• Transparency 2.1.12
• 1 sheet of paper and pencil per pair of students

ACTIVITY

13 EXPAND ME

▶ **Structure**
• RallyCoach

▶ **Materials**
• Transparency 2.1.13
• 1 sheet of paper and pencil per pair of students

Numeric

1. Teacher poses many problems using Transparency 2.1.13.

2. Partner A expands the expression in problem one using multiplication, writing his/her response on the paper.

3. Partner B watches, listens, checks, and praises.

4. Partner B expands the expression in the next problem.

5. Partner A watches, listens, checks, and praises.

6. Repeat for remaining problems starting at step 2.

ACTIVITY

14 REWRITE USING EXPONENTS

▶ **Structure**
• RallyCoach

▶ **Materials**
• Transparency 2.1.14
• 1 sheet of paper and pencil per pair of students

Numeric

1. Teacher poses many problems using Transparency 2.1.14.

2. Partner A rewrites the expression in problem one using exponents, writing his/her response on the paper.

3. Partner B watches, listens, checks, and praises.

4. Partner B rewrites the expression in the next problem.

5. Partner A watches, listens, checks, and praises.

6. Repeat for remaining problems starting at step 2.

Cooperative Learning and Pre-Algebra: Becky Bride
Kagan Publishing • 1 (800) 933-2667 • www.KaganOnline.com

ACTIVITY 15
ORDER OF OPERATIONS

Numeric

Setup:
In pairs, Student A is the Sage; Student B is the Scribe. Students fold a sheet of paper in half and each writes his/her name on one half.

1. The Sage gives the Scribe step-by-step instructions on how to solve problem one.

2. The Scribe records the Sage's solution step-by-step in writing on the Sage's side of the paper.

3. If the Sage is correct, the Scribe praises the Sage. Otherwise, the Scribe coaches, then praises.

4. Students switch roles for the next problem.

▶ **Structure**
· Sage-N-Scribe

▶ **Materials**
· Transparency 2.1.15
· 1 sheet of paper and pencil per pair of students

ACTIVITY 16
WHAT DID WE LEARN?

Synthesis

1. Each teammate signs his/her name in the upper right corner of the team paper with the colored pen/pencil he/she is using.

2. One teammate writes "*Integers*" in the center of the team paper in a rectangle.

3. Teammate 1 shares with the team one core concept he/she learned in the unit.

4. The student checks for consensus.

5. The teammates show agreement or lack of agreement with thumbs up or down.

6. If there is agreement, the students celebrate and the teammate records the core concept on the graphic organizer, connecting it with a line to the main idea, *Integers*. If not, teammates discuss the response until there is agreement and then they celebrate.

7. Play continues with the next student's core concept, until all core concepts are exhausted.

8. Repeat steps 3–7 with teammates adding details to each core concept and making bridges between related ideas.

▶ **Structure**
· RoundTable Consensus

▶ **Materials**
· 1 large sheet of paper per team
· 1 different colored pen or pencil for each student in the team

Blackline 2.1.1

1 CAN YOU DEFINE ME?

Structure: Solo-Pair Consensus-Team Consensus

The set of integers is the set {. . . –3, –2, –1, 0, 1, 2, 3, . . .}.

1. Describe how this set of numbers is similar to the set of whole numbers.

2. Describe how the this set of numbers is different from the set of whole numbers.

3. Describe the type of numbers, which you have studied about in previous years, that are missing in this set.

4 Write your own definition for the set of integers.

5. Draw a diagram below that shows how the sets of natural numbers, whole numbers, integers, and real numbers are related.

Cooperative Learning and Pre-Algebra: Becky Bride
Kagan Publishing • 1 (800) 933-2667 • www.KaganOnline.com

CLASSIFY ME

Structure: RallyCoach

Classify each number by stating the set(s) of numbers to which it belongs.

1. 12

2. –9

3. 0

4. $\dfrac{2}{3}$

5. –15

6. 0.3

7. –8

8. 30

Answers:
1. natural, whole, integer, real   2. integer, real
3. whole, integer, real   4. real
5. integer, real   6. real
7. integer, real   8. natural, whole, integer, real

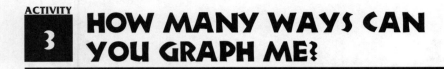

ACTIVITY 3
HOW MANY WAYS CAN YOU GRAPH ME?

Structure: RallyCoach

Graph each number on a number line, changing the scale of the number line each time it is graphed.

1. –24

2. –12

3. –18

4. –32

5. –48

6. –36

Answers will vary.

Cooperative Learning and Pre-Algebra: Becky Bride
Kagan Publishing • 1 (800) 933-2667 • www.KaganOnline.com

4 COMPARE ME

Structure: RallyCoach

For each problem:

a. Write a number sentence using the correct inequality symbol.

b. Using words, write a sentence as the inequality reads from left to right.

c. Using words, write a sentence as the inequality reads from right to left.

1. 9   –3   2. –16   3

3. –5   0   4. –2 –10

5. –12 –8   6.   4   7

7. –2 –15   8. –21 –23

Answers:
1. 9 > –3; Nine is greater than negative three; Negative three is less than nine.
2. –16 < 3; Negative sixteen is less than three; Three is greater than negative sixteen.
3. –5 < 0; Negative five is less than zero; Zero is greater than negative five.
4. –2 > –10; Negative two is greater than negative ten; Negative ten is less than negative two.
5. –12 < –8; Negative twelve is less than negative eight; Negative eight is greater than negative twelve.
6. 4 < 7; Four is less than seven; Seven is greater than four.
7. –2 > –15; Negative two is greater than negative fifteen; Negative fifteen is less than negative two.
8. –21 > –23; Negative twenty-one is greater than negative twenty-three; Negative twenty-three is less than negative twenty-one.

ACTIVITY
5 PLOT MY POINT

Structure: RallyCoach

Round 1: Graph each ordered pair on the coordinate plane on the front side of your paper, labeling it with its appropriate letter.

Round 2: Graph each ordered pair on a coordinate plane on the back side of your paper, labeling it with its appropriate letter.

A(2, –3)   B(–4, 0)   C(–3, –1)

D(–5, 2)   E(0, –8)   F(1, 3)

G(–6, 4)   H(0, 5)   I(2, 6)

J(–4, –5)   K(–3, 7)   L(5, –3)

Cooperative Learning and Pre-Algebra: Becky Bride
Kagan Publishing • 1 (800) 933-2667 • www.KaganOnline.com

6 **HOW MANY ORDERED PAIRS CAN YOU NAME?**

INTEGERS
2,-

Structure: RallyTable

Name as many ordered pairs that lie in the given quadrant or on the given axis.

1. Quadrant IV   2. Quadrant II

3. Negative *x*-axis   4. Quadrant I

5. Quadrant III   6. Negative *y*-axis

Answers will vary.

7 ADD ME

Structure: Sage-N-Scribe

Evaluate each of the following.

1. –3 + 8   2. 4 + (–2)

3. 5 + (–12)   4. –7 + (–8)

5. 12 + (–9)   6. –16 + (–13)

7. –4 + (–9)   8. –16 + 30

9. 8 + (–5) + 3   10. –16 + (–4) + 10

11. 13 + (–8) + 7 12. –6 + (–5) + (–12)

Answers:
1. 5   2. 2   3. –7   4. –15   5. 3   6. –29
7. –13   8. 14   9. 6   10. –10   11. 12   12. –23

Cooperative Learning and Pre-Algebra: Becky Bride
Kagan Publishing • 1 (800) 933-2667 • www.KaganOnline.com

ACTIVITY 8

SUBTRACT ME

Structure: Sage-N-Scribe

Evaluate each of the following.

1. $9 - (-3)$

2. $-2 - 6$

3. $5 - 7$

4. $13 - 16$

5. $12 - (-4)$

6. $-8 - 5$

7. $14 - 27$

8. $-21 - 8$

9. $-3 - 4 - (-7)$

10. $3 - 5 - 12$

11. $-9 - 3 - (-18)$

12. $16 - (-25) - 9$

Answers

1. 12	2. –8	3. –2	4. –3	5. 16	6. –13
7. –13	8. –29	9. 0	10. –14	11. 6	12. 32

MULTIPLY ME

Structure: Sage-N-Scribe

Evaluate each of the following.

1. $8(-3)$

2. $(-4)(-5)$

3. $(-11)(4)$

4. $(7)(3)$

5. $(-7)(-12)$

6. $3(-9)$

7. $4(-2)(-3)$

8. $(-5)(-6)(-3)$

9. $4(3)(-7)$

10. $(-8)(3)(-2)$

11. $(-3)(-7)(-10)$

12. $(-5)(-6)(4)$

Answers:
1. –24	2. 20	3. –44	4. 21	5. 84	6. –27
7. 24	8. –90	9. –84	10. 48	11. –210	12. 120

Cooperative Learning and Pre-Algebra: Becky Bride
Kagan Publishing • 1 (800) 933-2667 • www.KaganOnline.com

10 DIVIDE ME

Structure: Sage-N-Scribe

Evaluate each of the following.

1. $27 \div (-3)$ 2. $-32 \div 4$

3. $-45 \div (-9)$ 4. $18 \div (-3)$

5. $-9 \div (-3)$ 6. $-50 \div 10$

7. $48 \div 2$ 8. $-28 \div (-4)$

9. $60 \div (-6) \div 2$ 10. $-20 \div (-2) \div (-5)$

11. $-48 \div (-8) \div (-2)$ 12. $72 \div (-9) \div (-4)$

Answers:
1. –9   2. –8   3. 5   4. –6   5. 3   6. –5
7. 24   8. 7   9. –5   10. –2   11. –3   12. 2

ACTIVITY 11 INTEGER CARDS

Structure: Quiz-Quiz-Trade

0	1	2	3
4	5	6	7
8	9	10	11
12	13	14	15
16	17	18	19

Cooperative Learning and Pre-Algebra: Becky Bride
Kagan Publishing • 1 (800) 933-2667 • www.KaganOnline.com

11 INTEGER CARDS

Structure: Quiz-Quiz-Trade

–20	**–1**	**–2**	**–3**
–4	**–5**	**–6**	**–7**
–8	**–9**	**–10**	**–11**
–12	**–13**	**–14**	**–15**
–16	**–17**	**–18**	**–19**

ALL TOGETHER

Structure: Sage-N-Scribe

Perform the indicated operations.

1. $-4 - 3 + 8$ 2. $24 \div (-3)(-2)$

3. $-9 - 10(-3)$ 4. $-15 - (-5) + 6$

5. $12 \div (-2) - 6$ 6. $3(-2) - 8$

7. $-8 - (-9) - 16$ 8. $10 - 12 + (-3)$

9. $-36 \div (-4)(-3)$ 10. $13 - 21 \div (-3)$

11. $19 - 8 + (-7)$ 12. $3 - (-4) + (-9)$

Answers:
1. 1	2. 16	3. 21	4. −4	5. −12	6. −14
7. −15	8. −5	9. −27	10. 20	11. 4	12. −2

Cooperative Learning and Pre-Algebra: Becky Bride
Kagan Publishing • 1 (800) 933-2667 • www.KaganOnline.com

EXPAND ME

Structure: RallyCoach

Expand each of the following using multiplication.

1. -5^3

2. $(-6)^4$

3. $(-2)^7$

4. -3^3

5. -7^2

6. $(-4)^6$

7. $(-10)^5$

8. -8^2

Answers:
1. $-(5 \times 5 \times 5)$ 2. $(-6) \times (-6) \times (-6) \times (-6)$
3. $(-2)(-2)(-2)(-2)(-2)(-2)(-2)$ 4. $-(3 \times 3 \times 3)$
5. $-(7 \times 7)$ 6. $(-4)(-4)(-4)(-4)(-4)(-4)$
7. $(-10)(-10)(-10)(-10)(-10)$ 8. $-(8 \times 8)$

ACTIVITY

14 REWRITE USING EXPONENTS

Structure: RallyCoach

Rewrite each of the following using exponents.

1. $-11(-11)(-11)$

2. -4×4

3. $-3 \times 3 \times 3 \times 3$

4. $-8(-8)(-8)(-8)(-8)$

5. $-12 \times (-12)$

6. $-6 \times 6 \times 6 \times 6 \times 6 \times 6 \times 6$

7. $-9(9)(9)(9)(9)$

8. $-5 \times (-5) \times (-5)$

Answers:

1. $(-11)^3$	2. -4^2	3. -3^4	4. $(-8)^5$
5. $(-12)^2$	6. -6^7	7. -9^5	8. $(-5)^3$

Cooperative Learning and Pre-Algebra: Becky Bride
Kagan Publishing • 1 (800) 933-2667 • www.KaganOnline.com

ACTIVITY
15 **ORDER OF OPERATIONS**

INTEGERS
2,—

Structure: Sage-N-Scribe

Perform the indicated operations.

1. $-5^2 - 8(-2)$

2. $-7(1-5)^2 + 1$

3. $10 - (-3)^2 + 5$

4. $8(-2) - 3^2$

5. $\dfrac{-3(2-4)}{-6}$

6. $\dfrac{-42(2)}{9-13}$

7. $11 - (5-2)^2 \div 3$

8. $6 - (8+1)^2$

Answers:

1. −9	2. −111	3. 6	4. −25
5. −1	6. 21	7. 8	8. −75

LESSON 2:
EXPRESSIONS

This lesson begins with expanding expressions with an exponent whose coefficient is negative. This reinforces Activity 13 from Chapter 1, Lesson 1. The next activity has students rewrite expressions using exponents. Students will then work with inequality expressions, identifying which inequality fits their number and graphing inequality expressions on a number line. Activities 6 and 7 require students to simplify variable expressions. There are two wonderful exploratory activities in the book *Cooperative Learning and Algebra 1* that have students explore the meaning of like and unlike terms. These investigations would strengthen students' understanding of these concepts. Again, these were not included in this book to cut down duplication between the two books.

1 EXPAND MY VARIABLE EXPRESSION

▶ **Structure**
· RallyCoach

▶ **Materials**
· Transparency 2.2.1
· 1 sheet of paper and pencil per pair of students

Algebraic

1. Teacher poses many problems using Transparency 2.2.1.

2. Partner A expands the expression in problem one using multiplication, writing his/her response on the paper.

3. Partner B watches, listens, checks, and praises.

4. Partner B expands the expression in the next problem.

5. Partner A watches, listens, checks, and praises.

6. Repeat for remaining problems starting at step 2.

2 REWRITE MY VARIABLE EXPRESSION USING EXPONENTS

▶ **Structure**
· RallyCoach

▶ **Materials**
· Transparency 2.2.2
· 1 sheet of paper and pencil per pair of students

Algebraic

1. Teacher poses many problems using Transparency 2.2.2.

2. Partner A rewrites the expression in problem one using exponents, writing his/her response on the paper.

3. Partner B watches, listens, checks, and praises.

4. Partner B rewrites the expression in the next problem.

5. Partner A watches, listens, checks, and praises.

6. Repeat for remaining problems starting at step 2.

ACTIVITY 3

GRAPH ME ON THE NUMBER LINE

Graphic

Setup:

In pairs, Student A is the Sage; Student B is the Scribe. Students fold a sheet of paper in half and each writes his/her name on one half.

1. The Sage gives the Scribe step-by-step instructions on how to graph problem one on a number line.

2. The Scribe records the Sage's solution step-by-step in writing on the Sage's side of the paper.

3. If the Sage is correct, the Scribe praises the Sage. Otherwise, the Scribe coaches, then praises.

4. Students switch roles for the next problem.

▶ **Structure**
· Sage-N-Scribe

▶ **Materials**
· Transparency 2.2.3
· 1 sheet of paper, ruler and pencil per pair of students

ACTIVITY 4

WHERE DO YOU BELONG?

Algebraic

1. Teacher gives each student an integer card.

2. Students mix around the room trading cards.

3. Teacher announces different inequalities for each corner of the room using Transparency 2.2.4.

4. Students look at the number on their integer card, comparing it to each inequality.

5. Each student moves to the corner to which his/her number belongs.

6. Pairs are formed within each corner.

7. Using RallyRobin, pairs share the sum, product, or difference of the numbers on their card.

8. Students trade cards with someone in their corner.

9. Repeat steps 2–8 with the next set of inequalities on the transparency.

Note: During the corner phase, students could line up in numerical order, get in groups of three and find the sum, product, or difference of the numbers; or state to which set(s) the number(s) belong. This is an excellent opportunity for reviewing concepts.

▶ **Structure**
· Corners

▶ **Materials**
· Integer cards (Blackline 2.1.11)
· Transparency 2.2.4

ACTIVITY

5 EVALUATE ME

▶ **Structure**
• Sage-N-Scribe

▶ **Materials**
• Transparency 2.2.5
• 1 sheet of paper and pencil per pair of students

Algebraic

Setup:
In pairs, Student A is the Sage; Student B is the Scribe. Students fold a sheet of paper in half and each writes his/her name on one half.

1. The Sage gives the Scribe step-by-step instructions on how to evaluate problem one.

2. The Scribe records the Sage's solution step-by-step in writing on the Sage's side of the paper.

3. If the Sage is correct, the Scribe praises the Sage. Otherwise, the Scribe coaches, then praises.

4. Students switch roles for the next problem.

ACTIVITY

6 SIMPLIFY MY EXPRESSION

▶ **Structure**
• Sage-N-Scribe

▶ **Materials**
• Transparency 2.2.6
• 1 sheet of paper and pencil per pair of students

Algebraic

Setup:
In pairs, Student A is the Sage; Student B is the Scribe. Students fold a sheet of paper in half and each writes his/her name on one half.

1. The Sage gives the Scribe step-by-step instructions on how to simplify problem one.

2. The Scribe records the Sage's solution step-by-step in writing on the Sage's side of the paper.

3. If the Sage is correct, the Scribe praises the Sage. Otherwise, the Scribe coaches, then praises.

4. Students switch roles for the next problem.

Cooperative Learning and Pre-Algebra: Becky Bride
Kagan Publishing • 1 (800) 933-2667 • www.KaganOnline.com

ACTIVITY

7 SIMPLIFY MY EXPRESSION—TAKE 2

Algebraic

Setup:
Teacher gives each team a set of expression cards and a set of operation cards. The team separates the expression cards from the operation cards, mixes each stack, and places each stack facedown.

1. The teacher selects one student on each team to be the Showdown Captain for the first round.

2. The Showdown Captain draws 3 expression cards and 2 operation cards. He/she arranges the cards to form a trinomial. The captain asks each teammate to simplify the expression and provides think time.

3. Working alone, all students, including the Showdown Captain, simplify the expression.

4. When finished, teammates signal they're ready.

5. The Showdown Captain calls, "Showdown."

6. Teammates show and discuss their answers. The Showdown Captain leads the checking.

7. If correct, the team celebrates; if not, teammates tutor, then celebrate.

8. The person on the left of the Showdown Captain becomes the new Showdown Captain for the next round.

9. Steps 2–8 are repeated.

> ▶ **Structure:**
> • Showdown
>
> ▶ **Materials**
> • 1 set of Expression and Operation Cards per team (Blackline 2.2.7)
> • 1 sheet of paper and pencil per student

8 WHAT DID WE LEARN?

▶ **Structure**
• RoundTable Consensus

▶ **Materials**
• 1 large sheet of paper per team
• 1 different colored pen or pencil for each student in the team

Synthesis

1. Each teammate signs his/her name in the upper right corner of the team paper with the colored pen/pencil he/she is using.

2. One teammate writes *"Integer Expressions"* in the center of the team paper in a rectangle.

3. Teammate 1 shares with the team one core concept he/she learned in the unit.

4. The student checks for consensus.

5. The teammates show agreement or lack of agreement with thumbs up or down.

6. If there is agreement, the students celebrate and the teammate records the core concept on the graphic organizer, connecting it with a line to the main idea, *Integer Expressions.* If not, teammates discuss the response until there is agreement and then they celebrate.

7. Play continues with the next student's core concept, until all core concepts are exhausted.

8. Repeat steps 3–7 with teammates adding details to each core concept and making bridges between related ideas.

Cooperative Learning and Pre-Algebra: Becky Bride
Kagan Publishing • 1 (800) 933-2667 • www.KaganOnline.com

EXPAND MY VARIABLE EXPRESSION

Structure: RallyCoach

Expand each of the following using multiplication.

1. $(-p)^3$

2. $-k^2$

3. $-5x^4$

4. $(-2x)^3$

5. $-m^5$

6. $-3y^4$

7. $(-4j)^2$

8. $-w^5$

Answers:

1. $-p(-p)(-p)$

2. $-k(k)$

3. $-5(x)(x)(x)(x)$

4. $-2x(-2x)(-2x)$

5. $-m \times m \times m \times m \times m$

6. $-3 \times y \times y \times y \times y$

7. $-4j(-4j)$

8. $-w \times w \times w \times w \times w$

REWRITE MY VARIABLE EXPRESSION USING EXPONENTS

Structure: RallyCoach

Rewrite each of the following using exponents.

1. $-d \times d \times d$

2. $-n(-n)(-n)(-n)$

3. $-c(-c)(-c)(-c)(-c)$

4. $-w \times w$

5. $-2r(2r)$

6. $-3k(-3k)(-3k)$

7. $-h(h)(h)(h)$

8. $-7g(7g)(7g)(7g)$

Answers:

1. $-d^3$	2. $(-n)^4$	3. $(-c)^5$	4. $-w^2$
5. $-(2r)^2$	6. $(-3k)^3$	7. $-h^4$	8. $-(7g)^4$

Cooperative Learning and Pre-Algebra: Becky Bride
Kagan Publishing • 1 (800) 933-2667 • www.KaganOnline.com

GRAPH ME ON THE NUMBER LINE

Structure: Sage-N-Scribe

Graph each inequality on a different number line.

1. $x \geq (-4)$ 2. $2 > x$

3. $-3 < x$ 4. $p \geq (-10)$

5. $-5 < w \leq 2$ 6. $9 \geq u > (-1)$

7. $-3 > v \geq (-10)$ 8. $-8 \leq y < (-2)$

Answers will vary.

Cooperative Learning and Pre-Algebra: Becky Bride
Kagan Publishing • 1 (800) 933-2667 • www.KaganOnline.com

ACTIVITY

4 WHERE DO YOU BELONG?

Structure: Corners

Round 1

Corner 1: $-20 < x \leq (-5)$ Corner 2: $-5 < x < 2$

Corner 3: $2 \leq x \leq 11$ Corner 4: $11 < x$

Round 2

Corner 1: $x > 12$ Corner 2: $12 \geq x \geq 1$

Corner 3: $1 > x > (-7)$ Corner 4: $-7 \geq x$

Round 3

Corner 1: $x < (-8)$ Corner 2: $-8 \leq x < (-1)$

Corner 3: $5 > x \geq (-1)$ Corner 4: $x \geq 5$

Round 4

Corner 1: $x \geq 14$ Corner 2: $14 > x \geq 0$

Corner 3: $-11 \leq x < 0$ Corner 4: $x < (-11)$

Cooperative Learning and Pre-Algebra: Becky Bride
Kagan Publishing • 1 (800) 933-2667 • www.KaganOnline.com

EVALUATE ME

Structure: Sage-N-Scribe

Evaluate each of the following if
$w = (-4)$, $x = 3$, and $h = (-2)$.

1. $4w^2 - x$

2. $-h^5 - wx$

3. $\dfrac{(xh)^2}{w}$

4. $x - \dfrac{w^3}{h}$

5. $2w - h^3 + 3x$

6. $h^3(2w - x)$

7. $\dfrac{4x^2 - w}{h^2}$

8. $x^2 - 3wh$

Answers:
1. 61	2. 44	3. −9	4. −29
5. 9	6. 88	7. 10	8. −15

SIMPLIFY MY EXPRESSION

Structure: Sage-N-Scribe

Simply each expression.

1. $4x - 3y - 5x$

2. $7u^2 - 2u + 4u$

3. $-9x^2 - 6 - 2x + 4$

4. $(-w)^2 + 2w - 3w^2$

5. $8 - h^3 - 3h^3$

6. $5xy - 3y + 7y$

7. $6 - 8x + 5x - 2^3$

8. $3p^2 - (-p)^2 - p^2$

Answers:

1. $-x - 3y$ 2. $7u^2 + 2u$ 3. $-9x^2 - 2x - 2$ 4. $-2w^2 + 2w$
5. $8 - 4h^3$ 6. $5xy + 4y$ 7. $-2 - 3x$ 8. p^2

Cooperative Learning and Pre-Algebra: Becky Bride
Kagan Publishing • 1 (800) 933-2667 • www.KaganOnline.com

Structure: Showdown

Expression Cards

$5w$	$-w^2$	7	$-h^3$
$-6w$	$5w^2$	-6	$(2h)^3$
$9w$	$3w^2$	-1	$3h^3$
$2w$	$-4w^2$	8	$5h^3$
$-w$	$10w^2$	3	$4h^3$
$8w$	$9w^2$	10	$-7h^3$

SIMPLIFY MY EXPRESSION–TAKE 2

Structure: Showdown

Expression Cards

+	+	+	+
+	+	+	+
−	−	−	−
−	−	−	−

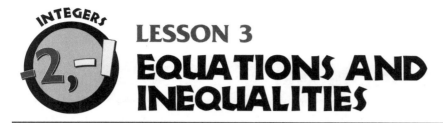

LESSON 3
EQUATIONS AND INEQUALITIES

This lesson begins with solving one-step, then two-step, equations whose coefficients and constants are integers. This reinforces Lesson 3 from Chapter 1. The next activity has students determine whether the inequality sign needs to be flipped to solve a one-step inequality. There is a wonderful exploratory activity in the book *Cooperative Learning and Algebra 1* that has students explore the need to flip the inequality symbol when multiplying or dividing by a negative number. This investigation would strengthen students' understanding of this concept. Again, this was not included in this book to cut down duplicity between the two books. The next several activities have students solve one, and two-step inequalities. Activity 6 has students find mistakes in completed problems which has them look at solving inequalities from a different perspective. The lesson wraps up with a synthesis activity.

SOLVE MY EQUATION

Algebraic

Setup:

In pairs, Student A is the Sage; Student B is the Scribe. Students fold a sheet of paper in half and each writes his/her name on one half.

1. The Sage gives the Scribe step-by-step instructions on how to solve problem one.

2. The Scribe records the Sage's solution step-by-step in writing on the Sage's side of the paper.

3. If the Sage is correct, the Scribe praises the Sage. Otherwise, the Scribe coaches, then praises.

4. Students switch roles for the next problem.

▶ **Structure**
· Sage-N-Scribe

▶ **Materials**
· Transparency 2.3.1
· 1 sheet of paper and pencil per pair of students

ACTIVITY

2

CAN YOU SOLVE ME?

▶ **Structure**
• Sage-N-Scribe

▶ **Materials**
• Transparency 2.3.2
• 1 sheet of paper and pencil per pair of students

Algebraic

Setup:
In pairs, Student A is the Sage; Student B is the Scribe. Students fold a sheet of paper in half and each writes his/her name on one half.

1. The Sage gives the Scribe step-by-step instructions on how to solve problem one.

2. The Scribe records the Sage's solution step-by-step in writing on the Sage's side of the paper.

3. If the Sage is correct, the Scribe praises the Sage. Otherwise, the Scribe coaches, then praises.

4. Students switch roles for the next problem.

ACTIVITY

3

DOES MY SIGN NEED TO FLIP?

▶ **Structure**
• RallyCoach

▶ **Materials**
• Transparency 2.3.3
• 1 sheet of paper and pencil per pair of students

Algebraic

1. Teacher poses many problems using Transparency 2.3.3.

2. Partner A determines whether the inequality sign needs to flip in problem one and writes a sentence explaining why it flips or why it doesn't flip.

3. Partner B watches, listens, checks, and praises.

4. Partner B determines whether the inequality sign needs to flip in the next problem and writes a sentence explaining why it flips or why it doesn't flip.

5. Partner A watches, listens, checks, and praises.

6. Repeat for remaining problems starting at step 2.

Cooperative Learning and Pre-Algebra: Becky Bride
Kagan Publishing • 1 (800) 933-2667 • www.KaganOnline.com

ACTIVITY
4

SOLVE MY ONE-STEP INEQUALITY

Algebraic/Graphic

Setup:
In pairs, Student A is the Sage; Student B is the Scribe. Students fold a sheet of paper in half and each writes his/her name on one half.

1. The Sage gives the Scribe step-by-step instructions on how to solve problem one and how to graph the answer on a number line.

2. The Scribe records the Sage's solution step-by-step in writing on the Sage's side of the paper.

3. If the Sage is correct, the Scribe praises the Sage. Otherwise, the Scribe coaches, then praises.

4. Students switch roles for the next problem.

▶ **Structure**
• Sage-N-Scribe

▶ **Materials**
• Transparency 2.3.4
• 1 sheet of paper and pencil per pair of students

ACTIVITY
5

SOLVE MY TWO-STEP INEQUALITY

Algebraic/Graphic

Setup:
In pairs, Student A is the Sage; Student B is the Scribe. Students fold a sheet of paper in half and each writes his/her name on one half.

1. The Sage gives the Scribe step-by-step instructions on how to solve problem one and how to graph the answer on a number line.

2. The Scribe records the Sage's solution step-by-step in writing on the Sage's side of the paper.

3. If the Sage is correct, the Scribe praises the Sage. Otherwise, the Scribe coaches, then praises.

4. Students switch roles for the next problem.

▶ **Structure**
• Sage-N-Scribe

▶ **Materials**
• Transparency 2.3.5
• 1 sheet of paper and pencil per pair of students

ACTIVITY

6 FIND MY MISTAKES

▶ **Structure:**
· RallyCoach

▶ **Materials**
· Transparency 2.3.6
· 1 sheet of paper and pencil per pair of students

Algebraic

1. Teacher poses many problems using Transparency 2.3.6.

2. Partner A finds the mistake(s) in problem one, describing them on the paper.

3. Partner B watches, listens, checks, and praises.

4. Partner B finds the mistake(s) and describes them on paper for the next problem.

5. Partner A watches, listens, checks, and praises.

6. Repeat for remaining problems starting at step 2.

ACTIVITY

7 WHAT DID WE LEARN?

▶ **Structure**
· RoundTable Consensus

▶ **Materials:**
· 1 large sheet of paper per team
· 1 different colored pen or pencil for each student in the team

Synthesis

1. Each teammate signs his/her name in the upper right corner of the team paper with the colored pen/pencil he/she is using.

2. One teammate writes "*Integer Equations and Inequalities*" in the center of the team paper in a rectangle.

3. Teammate 1 shares with the team one core concept he/she learned in the unit.

4. The student checks for consensus.

5. The teammates show agreement or lack of agreement with thumbs up or down.

6. If there is agreement, the students celebrate and the teammate records the core concept on the graphic organizer, connecting it with a line to the main idea, *Integer Equations and Inequalities*. If not, teammates discuss the response until there is agreement and then they celebrate.

7. Play continues with the next student's core concept, until all core concepts are exhausted.

8. Repeat steps 3–7 with teammates adding details to each core concept and making bridges between related ideas.

Cooperative Learning and Pre-Algebra: Becky Bride
Kagan Publishing • 1 (800) 933-2667 • www.KaganOnline.com

1 SOLVE MY EQUATION

Structure: Sage-N-Scribe

Solve each equation showing all work.

1. $-4 + y = 15$ 　　　　　　 2. $-5j = (-30)$

3. $\dfrac{c}{8} = (-4)$ 　　　　　　 4. $18 = m - 3$

5. $h - (-5) = 16$ 　　　　　　 6. $-21 = p + 7$

7. $42 = (-2x)$ 　　　　　　 8. $\dfrac{d}{-5} = 4$

9. $-8 + k = (-17)$ 　　　　　 10. $w - (-3) = (-8)$

Answers:
1. 19 　　2. 6 　　3. −32 　　4. 21 　　5. 11
6. −28 　　7. −21 　　8. −20 　　9. −9 　　10. −11

Cooperative Learning and Pre-Algebra: Becky Bride
Kagan Publishing • 1 (800) 933-2667 • www.KaganOnline.com

ACTIVITY

2 CAN YOU SOLVE ME?

Structure: Sage-N-Scribe

Solve each problem, showing all work.

1. $4m - (-2) = 18$

2. $2 = 9 - \dfrac{w}{3}$

3. $\dfrac{u}{-2} + 11 = 9$

4. $9 - 2d = (-31)$

5. $-46 = (-6) + 5p$

6. $\dfrac{h}{9} - 5 = 6$

7. $-12g - (-7) = 31$

8. $-8w - (-3) = (-53)$

9. $2 - \dfrac{v}{3} = (-10)$

10. $-16 = \dfrac{c}{7} + 8$

Answers:

1. 4	2. 21	3. 4	4. 20	5. –8
6. 99	7. –2	8. 7	9. 36	10. –168

Cooperative Learning and Pre-Algebra: Becky Bride
Kagan Publishing • 1 (800) 933-2667 • www.KaganOnline.com

ACTIVITY
3 DOES MY SIGN NEED TO FLIP?

Structure: RallyCoach

Determine if the inequality sign needs to flip when solving the inequality and explain your thinking.

1. $m - 5 > 8$

2. $8y < (-40)$

3. $-2x \geq 22$

4. $\dfrac{w}{-4} > 16$

5. $-6 - p \leq 7$

6. $3k \geq (-15)$

7. $\dfrac{-k}{3} < (-16)$

8. $j + 7 < (-11)$

9. $\dfrac{-v}{-5} > (-10)$

10. $-k + 8 \leq (-9)$

Answers:
1. no   2. no   3. yes   4. yes   5. yes
6. no   7. yes   8. no   9. no   10. yes

Cooperative Learning and Pre-Algebra: Becky Bride
Kagan Publishing • 1 (800) 933-2667 • www.KaganOnline.com

SOLVE MY ONE-STEP INEQUALITY

Structure: Sage-N-Scribe

Solve each problem showing all work, and graph your answer on a number line.

1. $-5m < 10$

2. $14 \geq (-8) + x$

3. $y - 4 > 12$

4. $\dfrac{w}{-2} < 19$

5. $-19 \leq 8 + k$

6. $-9h > (-63)$

7. $\dfrac{n}{3} > (-20)$

8. $p - 7 \geq (-30)$

Answers:

1. $m > (-2)$	2. $x \leq 22$	3. $y > 16$	4. $w > (-38)$
5. $k \geq -27$	6. $h < 7$	7. $n > (-60)$	8. $p \geq (-23)$

Cooperative Learning and Pre-Algebra: Becky Bride
Kagan Publishing • 1 (800) 933-2667 • www.KaganOnline.com

SOLVE MY TWO-STEP INEQUALITY

Structure: Sage-N-Scribe

Solve each problem showing all work, and graph your answer on a number line.

1. $6 - 2x < 14$

2. $3m - 7 \leq (-31)$

3. $\dfrac{h}{5} + 2 \leq (-7)$

4. $75 \geq 3 - 12p$

5. $-35 < 5 - 8d$

6. $-1 < 16 - \dfrac{w}{6}$

7. $11 - y \geq 3$

8. $5c - 1 \leq (-51)$

9. $7 > 1 - \dfrac{v}{-5}$

10. $12 - n > 30$

Answers:
1. $x > (-4)$ 2. $m \leq (-8)$ 3. $h \leq (-45)$ 4. $p \geq -6$
5. $d < 5$ 6. $w < 102$ 7. $y \leq 8$ 8. $c \leq (-10)$
9. $v < 30$ 10. $n < (-18)$

ACTIVITY 6 **FIND MY MISTAKES?**

Structure: RallyCoach

Find and describe the mistakes made in the problems below.

1. $3x - 6 \geq (-15)$
   $\quad +6 \qquad +6$
   $\quad 3x \geq (-21)$
   $\quad \dfrac{3x}{3} \geq \dfrac{(-21)}{3}$
   $\quad x \quad \leq \dfrac{(-7)}{3}$

2. $9 - \dfrac{h}{2} < 8$
   $\quad -9 \qquad -9$
   $\quad -\dfrac{h}{2} < (-1)$
   $\quad h < (-2)$

3. $(-3) - \dfrac{u}{5} \geq 1$
   $\qquad \times 5 \qquad \times 5$
   $\quad (-3) - u \geq 5$
   $\quad -3 \qquad -3$
   $\qquad -u \geq 2$
   $\quad \times (-1) \quad \times (-1)$
   $\qquad u \leq (-2)$

4. $12 \geq (-8) - 2m$
   $\quad \dfrac{12}{2} \geq (-8) - \dfrac{2m}{2}$
   $\quad -6 \geq (-8) - m$
   $\quad +8 \qquad +8$
   $\quad 2 \geq (-m)$
   $\quad \times (-1) \quad \times (-1)$
   $\quad (-2) \geq m$

Cooperative Learning and Pre-Algebra: Becky Bride
Kagan Publishing • 1 (800) 933-2667 • www.KaganOnline.com

DECIMALS

3.6

DECIMALS

This chapter works with decimals. It spirals the pre-algebra/algebra concepts that were introduced in Chapter 1. The first lesson on number sense has students classify, compare, and round decimals. Students will graph decimal numbers and ordered pairs. The four arithmetic operations are performed with decimals. Lesson 2 reinforces evaluating and simplifying expressions, but this time the coefficients are decimals. The last lesson has students solving equations and inequalities with decimal coefficients and constants. Each lesson ends with a synthesis activity so students can summarize what they learned.

LESSON

1 NUMBER SENSE

ACTIVITY 1: Classify Me
ACTIVITY 2: Identify My Place Value
ACTIVITY 3: Round Me
ACTIVITY 4: Write Me Using Words
ACTIVITY 5: Compare Me
ACTIVITY 6: Compare Me Again
ACTIVITY 7: What Am I Between?
ACTIVITY 8: How Many Ways Can You Graph Me?
ACTIVITY 9: Plot My Point
ACTIVITY 10: Add Me
ACTIVITY 11: Subtract Me
ACTIVITY 12: Multiply Me
ACTIVITY 13: Divide Me
ACTIVITY 14: Expand Me
ACTIVITY 15: Rewrite Me
ACTIVITY 16: Evaluate Me
ACTIVITY 17: Applications
ACTIVITY 18: What Did We Learn?

LESSON

2 EXPRESSIONS

ACTIVITY 1: Graph My Inequality
ACTIVITY 2: Where Do You Belong?
ACTIVITY 3: Evaluate My Expression
ACTIVITY 4: Simplify My Expression
ACTIVITY 5: Geometric Applications
ACTIVITY 6: What Did We Learn?

LESSON

3 EQUATIONS AND INEQUALITIES

ACTIVITY 1: Solve My One-Step Equation
ACTIVITY 2: Solve My Two-Step Equation
ACTIVITY 3: Solve My One-Step Inequality
ACTIVITY 4: Solve My Two-Step Inequality
ACTIVITY 5: Apply Me
ACTIVITY 6: What Did We Learn?

LESSON 1
NUMBER SENSE

This lesson begins with introducing decimals as part of the rational set of numbers in the real number system. Activity 1 has students classify numbers that belong to the natural, whole, integer, rational, and/or real number sets, thus reinforcing the sets studied in Chapters 1 and 2. Students will compare decimals. Place value is processed in Activities 2 and 3. Decimals are then graphed on both a number line and coordinate plane. Activities 10–14 have students practice addition, subtraction, multiplication, and division with decimals. Activities 14 and 15 are included to reinforce the concept of exponents and the difference between the opposite of a number raised to a power and a negative decimal raised to a power. Activity 16 requires students to use their understanding from Activities 14 and 15 to perform the order of operations. This lesson ends with applications and an activity to synthesize the lesson.

ACTIVITY 1
CLASSIFY ME

▶ **Structure**
• RallyCoach

▶ **Materials**
• Transparency 3.1.1
• 1 sheet of paper and pencil per pair of students

Numeric

1. Teacher poses many problems using Transparency 3.1.1.

2. Partner A classifies the number in problem one as a natural, whole, integer, rational, and/or real number, writing his/her response on the paper.

3. Partner B watches, listens, checks, and praises.

4. Partner B classifies the number in the next problem.

5. Partner A watches, listens, checks, and praises.

6. Repeat for remaining problems starting at step 2.

ACTIVITY 2
IDENTIFY MY PLACE VALUE

▶ **Structure**
• RallyCoach

▶ **Materials:**
• Transparency 3.1.2
• 1 sheet of paper and pencil per pair of students

Numeric

1. Teacher poses many problems using Transparency 3.1.2.

2. Partner A identifies the place value of the underlined number in problem one, writing his/her response on the paper.

3. Partner B watches, listens, checks, and praises.

4. Partner B identifies the place value in the next problem, writing his/her response on the paper.

5. Partner A watches, listens, checks, and praises.

6. Repeat for remaining problems starting at step 2.

Cooperative Learning and Pre-Algebra: Becky Bride
Kagan Publishing • 1 (800) 933-2667 • www.KaganOnline.com

ROUND ME

This activity can be done in several rounds. In the first round, students round the numbers to the tenths place. In round 2, the students round the numbers to the thousandths place. In round 3, the students round the numbers to the nearest whole number. In round 4, the students round the numbers to the hundredths place.

Numeric

1. Teacher poses many problems using Transparency 3.1.2.

2. Partner A rounds the number to the requested place in problem one, writing his/her response on the paper.

3. Partner B watches, listens, checks, and praises.

4. Partner B rounds the number in the next problem, writing his/her response on the paper.

5. Partner A watches, listens, checks, and praises.

6. Repeat for remaining problems starting at step 2.

7. Repeat for remaining rounds starting at step 2.

▶ **Structure**
• RallyCoach

▶ **Materials**
• Transparency 3.1.2
• 1 sheet of paper and pencil per pair of students

WRITE ME USING WORDS

This activity is a preparatory activity for Activity 5. It has students write decimals using words since students will have to write two sentences in the activity, Compare Me.

Numeric

Setup:
In pairs, Student A is the Sage; Student B is the Scribe. Students fold a sheet of paper in half and each writes his/her name on one half.

1. The Sage gives the Scribe step-by-step instructions on how to write the number in words for problem one.

2. The Scribe records the Sage's description in writing on the Sage's side of the paper.

3. If the Sage is correct, the Scribe praises the Sage. Otherwise, the Scribe coaches, then praises.

4. Students switch roles for the next problem.

▶ **Structure**
• Sage-N-Scribe

▶ **Materials**
• Transparency 3.1.3
• 1 sheet of paper and pencil per pair of students

Chapter 3: Decimals

Lesson One

ACTIVITY 5

COMPARE ME

▶ **Structure**
• RallyCoach

▶ **Materials**
• Transparency 3.1.4
• 1 sheet of paper and pencil per pair of students

Numeric

1. Teacher poses many problems using Transparency 3.1.4.

2. Partner A compares the two numbers in problem one and writes the problem, inserting the correct inequality symbol. Then he/she writes the expression as a sentence as the inequality would be read from left to right. He/she writes a second sentence as the inequality would be read from right to left.

3. Partner B watches, listens, checks, and praises.

4. Partner B repeats step 2 for the next problem.

5. Partner A watches, listens, checks, and praises.

6. Repeat for remaining problems starting at step 2.

ACTIVITY 6

COMPARE ME AGAIN

▶ **Structure**
• RoundTable Consensus

▶ **Materials**
• 1 set of Decimal Cards (Blackline 3.1.5) per team
• 1 set of inequality cards (Blackline 1.1.5) per team

Numeric

Setup:
Blacklines 1.1.5 and 3.1.5 need to be copied onto two different colors of cardstock—one for the Decimal Cards and one for the Inequality Cards, then cut into individual cards. Cards are distributed to each team of students.

1. Teammate 1 mixes the decimal cards and places them in a stack on the table. The inequality cards are in a stack, faceup.

2. Each teammate draws a decimal card.

3. Teammate 2 arranges the drawn decimal cards with the correct inequality cards he/she

has chosen from the inequality card stack. Teammate 2 explains to his/her team why the cards are placed in that order. The teammate checks for consensus.

4. The teammates show agreement or lack of agreement with thumbs up or down.

5. If there is agreement, the students celebrate and steps 2–5 are repeated, rotating one teammate each time. If not, the teammates discuss the response until there is agreement and then they celebrate. If no agreement is reached, the cards are set aside to be discussed later.

6. Repeat steps 2–5, rotating 1 teammate each time.

Cooperative Learning and Pre-Algebra: Becky Bride
Kagan Publishing • 1 (800) 933-2667 • www.KaganOnline.com

ACTIVITY
7 WHAT AM I BETWEEN?

This activity can be done in several rounds. Each round, change the place value of the last digit of each number. Answers are provided for tenths, hundredths, and thousandths places.

Numeric

1. Teacher poses many problems using Transparency 3.1.6.

2. Partner A writes 2 numbers that are the closest to the number in problem one, such that the number in problem one falls between these 2 numbers and the last digit of each number is in the requested place value, writing his/her response on the paper.

3. Partner B watches, listens, checks, and praises.

4. Partner B writes 2 numbers that are the closest to the number in the next problem, such that the number in the next problem falls between these 2 numbers and the last digit of each number is in the requested place value, writing his/her response on the paper.

5. Partner A watches, listens, checks, and praises.

6. Repeat for remaining problems starting at step 2.

7. Repeat for remaining rounds starting at step 2.

▶ **Structure**
• RallyCoach

▶ **Materials**
• Transparency 3.1.6
• 1 sheet of paper and pencil per pair of students

ACTIVITY
8 HOW MANY WAYS CAN YOU GRAPH ME?

Graphic

1. Teacher poses many problems using Transparency 3.1.7.

2. Partner A graphs the number in the first problem on a number line, using any scale he/she chooses.

3. Partner B watches, listens, checks, and praises.

4. Partner B graphs the same number on a different number line using a different scale of his/her choice.

5. Partner A watches, listens, checks, and praises.

6. Repeat until three graphs are graphed for problem one.

7. Repeat for remaining problems starting at step 2.

▶ **Structure**
• RallyCoach

▶ **Materials**
• Transparency 3.1.7
• 1 sheet of paper, pencil, and ruler per pair of students

ACTIVITY
9 PLOT MY POINT

▶ **Structure**
· RallyCoach

▶ **Materials**
· Transparency 3.1.8
· 1-2 sheets of graph paper and pencil per pair of students

Graphic

1. Teacher poses many problems using Transparency 3.1.8.

2. Partner A graphs the point in the first problem on a coordinate plane, using any scale he/she chooses.

3. Partner B watches, listens, checks, and praises.

4. Partner B graphs the same point on a different coordinate plane, using a different scale for each axis of his/her choice.

5. Partner A watches, listens, checks, and praises.

6. Repeat until three graphs, with different scales, are graphed for problem one.

7. Repeat for remaining problems starting at step 2.

ACTIVITY
10 ADD ME

▶ **Structure**
· Sage-N-Scribe

▶ **Materials**
· Transparency 3.1.9
· 1 sheet of paper and pencil per pair of students

Numeric

Setup:
In pairs, Student A is the Sage; Student B is the Scribe. Students fold a sheet of paper in half and each writes his/her name on one half.

1. The Sage gives the Scribe step-by-step instructions on how to add the numbers in problem one.

2. The Scribe records the Sage's solution step-by-step in writing on the Sage's side of the paper.

3. If the Sage is correct, the Scribe praises the Sage. Otherwise, the Scribe coaches, then praises.

4. Students switch roles for the next problem.

Cooperative Learning and Pre-Algebra: Becky Bride
Kagan Publishing • 1 (800) 933-2667 • www.KaganOnline.com

ACTIVITY
11 **SUBTRACT ME**

Numeric

Setup:

In pairs, Student A is the Sage; Student B is the Scribe. Students fold a sheet of paper in half and each writes his/her name on one half.

1. The Sage gives the Scribe step-by-step instructions on how to subtract the numbers in problem one.

2. The Scribe records the Sage's solution step-by-step in writing on the Sage's side of the paper.

3. If the Sage is correct, the Scribe praises the Sage. Otherwise, the Scribe coaches, then praises.

4. Students switch roles for the next problem.

▶ **Structure**
• Sage-N-Scribe

▶ **Materials**
• Transparency 3.1.10
• 1 sheet of paper and pencil per pair of students

ACTIVITY
12 **MULTIPLY ME**

Numeric

Setup:

In pairs, Student A is the Sage; Student B is the Scribe. Students fold a sheet of paper in half and each writes his/her name on one half.

1. The Sage gives the Scribe step-by-step instructions on how to multiply the numbers in problem one.

2. The Scribe records the Sage's solution step-by-step in writing on the Sage's side of the paper.

3. If the Sage is correct, the Scribe praises the Sage. Otherwise, the Scribe coaches, then praises.

4. Students switch roles for the next problem.

▶ **Structure**
• Sage-N-Scribe

▶ **Materials**
• Transparency 3.1.11
• 1 sheet of paper and pencil per pair of students

Chapter 3: Decimals
Lesson One

DECIMALS

3.6

DIVIDE ME

▶ **Structure**
· Sage-N-Scribe

▶ **Materials**
· Transparency 3.1.12
· 1 sheet of paper and pencil per pair of students

Numeric

Setup:
In pairs, Student A is the Sage; Student B is the Scribe. Students fold a sheet of paper in half and each writes his/her name on one half.

1. The Sage gives the Scribe step-by-step instructions on how to divide the numbers in problem one.

2. The Scribe records the Sage's solution step-by-step in writing on the Sage's side of the paper.

3. If the Sage is correct, the Scribe praises the Sage. Otherwise, the Scribe coaches, then praises.

4. Students switch roles for the next problem.

ACTIVITY

EXPAND ME

▶ **Structure**
· RallyCoach

▶ **Materials**
· Transparency 3.1.13
· 1 sheet of paper and pencil per pair of students

Numeric

1. Teacher poses many problems using Transparency 3.1.13.

2. Partner A expands the expression in problem one using multiplication, writing his/her response on the paper.

3. Partner B watches, listens, checks, and praises.

4. Partner B expands the expression in the next problem using multiplication, writing his/her response on the paper.

5. Partner A watches, listens, checks, and praises.

6. Repeat for remaining problems starting at step 2.

Chapter 3: Decimals
Lesson One

Cooperative Learning and Pre-Algebra: Becky Bride
Kagan Publishing • 1 (800) 933-2667 • www.KaganOnline.com

15 REWRITE ME

Numeric

1. Teacher poses many problems using Transparency 3.1.14.

2. Partner A rewrites the expression in problem one using exponents, writing his/her response on the paper.

3. Partner B watches, listens, checks, and praises.

4. Partner B rewrites the expression in the next problem using exponents, writing his/her response on the paper.

5. Partner A watches, listens, checks, and praises.

6. Repeat for remaining problems starting at step 2.

▶ **Structure**
• RallyCoach

▶ **Materials**
• Transparency 3.1.14
• 1 sheet of paper and pencil per pair of students

16 EVALUATE ME

Numeric

Setup:
In pairs, Student A is the Sage; Student B is the Scribe. Students fold a sheet of paper in half and each writes his/her name on one half.

1. The Sage gives the Scribe step-by-step instructions on how to evaluate problem one.

2. The Scribe records the Sage's solution step-by-step in writing on the Sage's side of the paper.

3. If the Sage is correct, the Scribe praises the Sage. Otherwise, the Scribe coaches, then praises.

4. Students switch roles for the next problem.

▶ **Structure**
• Sage-N-Scribe

▶ **Materials**
• Transparency 3.1.15
• 1 sheet of paper and pencil per pair of students

ACTIVITY

17 APPLICATIONS

▶ **Structure**
• Sage-N-Scribe

▶ **Materials**
• Blackline 3.1.16
• 1 sheet of paper and pencil per pair of students

Numeric

Setup:
In pairs, Student A is the Sage; Student B is the Scribe. Students fold a sheet of paper in half and each writes his/her name on one half.

1. The Sage gives the Scribe step-by-step instructions on how to solve problem one.

2. The Scribe records the Sage's solution step-by-step in writing on the Sage's side of the paper.

3. If the Sage is correct, the Scribe praises the Sage. Otherwise, the Scribe coaches, then praises.

4. Students switch roles for the next problem.

ACTIVITY

18 WHAT DID WE LEARN?

▶ **Structure**
• RoundTable Consensus

▶ **Materials**
• 1 large sheet of paper per team
• 1 different colored pen or pencil for each student in the team

Synthesis

1. Each teammate signs his/her name in the upper right corner of the team paper with the colored pen/pencil he/she is using.

2. One teammate writes "*Decimals*" in the center of the team paper in a rectangle.

3. Teammate 1 shares with the team one core concept he/she learned in the unit.

4. The student checks for consensus.

5. The teammates show agreement or lack of agreement with thumbs up or down.

6. If there is agreement, the students celebrate and the teammate records the core concept on the graphic organizer, connecting it with a line to the main idea, *Decimals*. If not, teammates discuss the response until there is agreement and then they celebrate.

7. Play continues with the next student's core concept, until all core concepts are exhausted.

8. Repeat steps 3–7 with teammates adding details to each core concept and making bridges between related ideas.

Cooperative Learning and Pre-Algebra: Becky Bride
Kagan Publishing • 1 (800) 933-2667 • www.KaganOnline.com

1 CLASSIFY ME

DECIMALS
3.6

Structure: RallyCoach

Classify each number by stating the set(s) of numbers to which it belongs.

1. –5.1

2. 4.00

3. 3.2

4. 0.9

5. 0

6. –0.01

7. –8

8. 13.081

9. 16.0

10. –9

Answers:

1. rational, real
2. natural, whole, integer, rational, real
3. rational, real
4. rational, real
5. whole, integer, rational, real
6. rational, real
7. integer, rational, real
8. rational, real
9. natural, whole, integer, rational, real
10. integer, rational, real

ACTIVITIES 2&3 IDENTIFY MY PLACE VALUE ROUND ME

DECIMALS 3.6

Structure: RallyCoach

Directions:
Activity 2: Identify the place value of the underlined number.
Activity 3: Round to the nearest place value announced by the teacher.

1. 103.2<u>9</u>81

2. 17<u>5</u>.1076

3. 536.<u>4</u>891

4. −<u>2</u>10.8362

5. −987.03<u>1</u>4

6. −6<u>5</u>3.1496

7. 738.<u>5</u>173

8. −272.834<u>6</u>

Answers:

Activity 2

1. hundredths	2. ones	3. tenths	4. hundreds
5. thousandths	6. tens	7. tenths	8. ten-thousandths

Activity 3

Round 1

1. 103.3	2. 175.1	3. 536.5	4. −210.8
5. −987.0	6. −653.1	7. 738.5	8. −272.8

Round 2

1. 103.298	2. 175.108	3. 536.489	4. −210.836
5. −987.031	6. −653.150	7. 738.517	8. −272.835

Round 3

1. 103	2. 175	3. 536	4. −211
5. −987	6. −653	7. 739	8. −273

Round 4

1. 103.30	2. 175.11	3. 536.49	4. −210.84
5. −987.03	6. −653.15	7. 738.52	8. −272.83

Cooperative Learning and Pre-Algebra: Becky Bride
Kagan Publishing • 1 (800) 933-2667 • www.KaganOnline.com

WRITE ME USING WORDS

Structure: Sage-N-Scribe

Write each number using words.

1. 3.4

2. 0.45

3. 1.298

4. –16.3

5. 0.0007

6. 7.015

7. –39.02

8. 2.0173

Answers:
1. three and four tenths
2. forty-five hundredths
3. one and two hundred ninety-eight thousandths
4. negative sixteen and three tenths
5. seven ten-thousandths
6. seven and fifteen thousandths
7. negative thirty-nine and two hundredths
8. two and one hundred seventy-three ten-thousandths

Cooperative Learning and Pre-Algebra: Becky Bride
Kagan Publishing • 1 (800) 933-2667 • www.KaganOnline.com

COMPARE ME

Structure: RallyCoach

For each problem:
a. **Write a number sentence using the correct inequality symbol.**

b. **Using words, write a sentence as the inequality reads from left to right.**

c. **Using words, write a sentence as the inequality reads from right to left.**

1. –27.7 __ –27.75   2. 4.9 __ 4.87

3. –8 __ –7.9   4. –8.00 __ –8

5. 3.07 __ 3.072   6. –6.342 __ –6.3

7. 10 __ 10.000   8. 11.405 __ 11.4

9. –0.83 __ –8.3   10. –15.34 __ –15.337

Answers:
1. >	2. >	3. <	4. =	5. <
6. <	7. =	8. >	9. >	10. <

Cooperative Learning and Pre-Algebra: Becky Bride
Kagan Publishing • 1 (800) 933-2667 • www.KaganOnline.com

ACTIVITY

6 COMPARE ME AGAIN

DECIMALS

3.6

Structure: RoundTable Consensus
Decimal Cards

–10.83	–10.8	–10	–7.43	–7.4	–5.92
–5.9	–4.41	–4.4	–3.95	–3.91	–2.21
–2.22	–2.1	–1.78	–1.7	–0.85	–0.81
1.3	1.47	2.01	2.3	2.37	3.6
3.61	3.9	4.1	4.17	4.2	5.7
5.76	6.7	6.78	7.56	7.58	7.6

ACTIVITY
7 **WHAT AM I BETWEEN?**

DECIMALS
3.6

Structure: RallyCoach

Choose two numbers that are closest to the given number, one on each side of the given number. The last digit of these two numbers will be the:
Round 1: tenths place
Round 2: hundredths place
Round 3: thousandths place.
Write answers from least to greatest.

1. 8.5	2. –3.67	3. –1.037
4. 0.5	5. –6.76	6. 5.493
7. 11.18	8. –27.38	

Answers:

Round 1	Round 2	Round 3
1. 8.4 & 8.6	1. 8.49 & 8.51	1. 8.499 & 8.501
2. –3.7 & –3.6	2. –3.68 & –3.66	2. –3.671 & –3.669
3. –1.1 & –1.0	3. –1.04 & –1.03	3. –1.038 & –1.036
4. 0.4 & 0.6	4. 0.49 & 0.51	4. 0.499 & 0.501
5. –6.8 & –6.7	5. –6.77 & –6.75	5. –6.761 & –6.759
6. 5.4 & 5.5	6. 5.49 & 5.50	6. 5.492 & 5.494
7. 11.1 & 11.2	7. 11.17 & 11.19	7. 11.179 & 11.181
8. –27.4 & –27.3	8. –27.39 & –27.37	8. –27.381 & –27.379

Cooperative Learning and Pre-Algebra: Becky Bride
Kagan Publishing • 1 (800) 933-2667 • www.KaganOnline.com

HOW MANY WAYS CAN YOU GRAPH ME?

Structure: RallyCoach

Graph each number on three different number lines using a different scale each time, alternating partners with each graph.

1. 5.6

2. –4.16

3. –2.7

4. 14.4

Answers will vary.

9 PLOT MY POINT

Structure: RallyCoach

Plot each point on different coordinate planes using different scales on the axes.

1. (1.2, –0.2)

2. (–0.24, –1.8)

3. (–0.16, 2.4)

4. (3.6, –0.8)

5. (0, 7.2)

6. (–4.8, 0)

7. (–2.4, –3.6)

8. (5.2, 6.4)

Answers will vary.

Cooperative Learning and Pre-Algebra: Becky Bride
Kagan Publishing • 1 (800) 933-2667 • www.KaganOnline.com

ACTIVITY
10 ADD ME

DECIMALS
3.6

Structure: Sage-N-Scribe

Evaluate each of the following.

1. $4.3 + 15.49$

2. $-27.5 + (-0.893)$

3. $-204.15 + (-4.798)$

4. $15 + 3.95$

5. $2.3 + 0.78 + 8$

6. $1.021 + 7 + 2.99$

7. $-2 + (-0.54) + (-1.8)$

8. $-34 + (-3.2) + (-0.11)$

9. $104 + 0.104 + 1.4$

10. $82 + 0.82 + 8.2$

Answers:

1. 19.79	2. −28.393	3. −208.948	4. 18.95	5. 11.08
6. 11.011	7. −4.34	8. −37.31	9. 105.504	10. 91.02

ACTIVITY

11 SUBTRACT ME

DECIMALS 3.6

Structure: Sage-N-Scribe

Evaluate each of the following.

1. –3.98 – 4.503

2. 15.08 –34.7

3. –1.11 – (–0.334)

4. –0.673 – (–4)

5. 3.6 – 0.681

6. 19 – 2.096

7. 8.2 – 23.09

8. 6.01 – (–3.877)

9. 2 – 2.4 –0.24

10. 6 – 9.8 – 2.44

Answers:
1. –8.483   2. –19.62   3. –0.776   4. 3.327   5. 2.919
6. 16.904   7. –14.89   8. 9.887   9. –0.64   10. –6.24

Cooperative Learning and Pre-Algebra: Becky Bride
Kagan Publishing • 1 (800) 933-2667 • www.KaganOnline.com

DECIMALS
3.6

Structure: Sage-N-Scribe

Evaluate each of the following.

1. 2.4 x 7.8

2. 0.31(–12)

3. –0.009(4.35)

4. 1.7 x 0.85

5. –0.13 x (–0.27)

6. 9.8(0.67)

7. (–3.4)(0.093)

8. –0.012(–4.3)

9. 2.8(4.09)

10. 8.3(–0.97)

Answers:
1. 18.72   2. –3.72   3. –0.03915   4. 1.445   5. 0.0351
6. 6.566   7. –0.3162   8. 0.0516   9. 11.452   10. –8.051

ACTIVITY

13 DIVIDE ME

DECIMALS
3.6

Structure: Sage-N-Scribe

Evaluate each of the following. Round to the thousandths place.

1. $\dfrac{4.7}{0.3}$

2. $\dfrac{0.583}{2}$

3. $-4.307 \div 0.9$

4. $-1.879 \div 0.08$

5. $\dfrac{3.17}{6}$

6. $\dfrac{6.07}{0.4}$

7. $-73.4 \div (-0.09)$

8. $87.9 \div (-0.3)$

Answers:
1. 15.667   2. 0.292   3. –4.786   4. –23.488
5. 0.528   6. 15.175   7. 815.556   8. –293

Cooperative Learning and Pre-Algebra: Becky Bride
Kagan Publishing • 1 (800) 933-2667 • www.KaganOnline.com

14 EXPAND ME

Structure: RallyCoach

Rewrite each of the following as a multiplication problem.

1. 4.3^2

2. $(-8.01)^5$

3. -0.17^8

4. -1.9^4

5. $(-3.2)^6$

6. 7.1^3

Answers:
1. 4.3(4.3)
2. (−8.01)(−8.01)(−8.01)(−8.01)(−8.01)
3. −0.17(0.17)(0.17)(0.17)(0.17)(0.17)(0.17)(0.17)
4. −1.9(1.9)(1.9)(1.9)
5. (−3.2)(−3.2)(−3.2)(−3.2)(−3.2)(−3.2)
6. 7.1(7.1)(7.1)

REWRITE ME

Structure: RallyCoach

Rewrite each using exponents.

1. $(-3.8)(-3.8)$

2. $-0.2(0.2)(0.2)(0.2)(0.2)(0.2)$

3. $6.37(6.37)(6.37)$

4. $11.4(11.4)(11.4)(11.4)$

5. $-2.3(2.3)(2.3)(2.3)(2.3)(2.3)(2.3)(2.3)$

6. $-9.1(-9.1)$

7. $0.4(0.4)(0.4)(0.4)(0.4)$

8. $-7.8(7.8)(7.8)(7.8)$

Answers:

1. $(-3.8)^2$	2. -0.2^6	3. 6.37^3	4. 11.4^4
5. -2.3^8	6. $(-9.1)^2$	7. 0.4^5	8. -7.8^4

Cooperative Learning and Pre-Algebra: Becky Bride
Kagan Publishing • 1 (800) 933-2667 • www.KaganOnline.com

16 EVALUATE ME

Structure: Sage-N-Scribe

Evaluate each of the following.

1. $2.1 + 3(-0.4)$

2. $0.24 \div 2^2(3)$

3. $-4(1.7 - 2.34)$

4. $-3 - \dfrac{1.2^2}{6}$

5. $0.9 - (-1.03)(2)$

6. $7.8 - (5.3 - 6.7)(2)$

7. $8 \div (-0.2) \times 7 - 0.5^2$

8. $(1.7 - 2)^2 + (-5.33)$

9. $0.06 - 0.48 \div 0.2(-3)$

10. $8.1 \div 27(-0.3)^2$

Answers:

1. 0.9	2. 0.18	3. 2.56	4. −3.24	5. 2.96
6. 10.6	7. −280.25	8. −5.24	9. 7.26	10. 0.027

17 APPLICATIONS

Structure: Sage-N-Scribe

Solve each problem.

1. Monica's checking account has a balance that started at $253.72. She made three deposits this month in the amounts of $27.16, $112.92, and $57.93. She wrote checks to pay bills in the amount of $35.03, $121.75, $68.14, and $109.12. What is her new checking account balance?

2. Anton bought two CDs at $16.99 each and three DVDs at $23.49 each. He gave the cashier $120. How much change did he get? Round to the nearest dollar.

3. Which is the better buy: an eight ounce box of pasta for $1.19 or a fifteen ounce box of pasta for $2.09?

4. Seana traveled three hundred eighty miles on a tank of gas that holds eleven gallons. How many miles per gallon does her car get? How many gallons would it take to drive nine hundred miles? Round to the nearest tenth.

5. Craig and his friends took a road trip. They travelled 3.5 hours at sixty miles per hour, 0.75 hours at forty-five miles per hour, and 2.1 hours at fifty miles per hour. How far did they travel? Round to the nearest mile.

Cooperative Learning and Pre-Algebra: Becky Bride
Kagan Publishing • 1 (800) 933-2667 • www.KaganOnline.com

ACTIVITY

 **17 APPLICATIONS**

Structure: Sage-N-Scribe

6. Saif want to tile his kitchen. His kitchen is rectangular and is 12.3 feet wide and 10.7 feet long. If tile costs $2.79 per square foot, how much will the tile cost? Round to the nearest cent.

7. Two cities on a map are 4.6 inches apart. If each inch on the map represents 25 miles, what is the actual distance between the two cities?

8. Cammie is building a doghouse. On the blueprint, each 0.25 inch is equivalent to 3.5 feet. If the length of the floor of the doghouse is .50 inches and the width is 0.25 inches on the blueprint, what is the area of the floor of the doghouse?

Answers:

1. $117.69	2. $15.55	3. 15 oz.	4. 34.5 mpg; 26.1 gallons
5. 349 miles	6. $367.19	7. 115 miles	8. 24.5 ft²

DECIMALS 3.6

LESSON 2
EXPRESSIONS

This lesson reinforces the expression lessons in the previous chapters. The coefficients and constants are decimals. The first two activities have students work with inequalities. The next several activities require students to evaluate variable expressions using rational numbers. The lesson ends with an application and a synthesis activity.

ACTIVITY

1 GRAPH MY INEQUALITY

▶ **Structure**
• Sage-N-Scribe

▶ **Materials**
• Transparency 3.2.1
• 1 sheet of paper and pencil per pair of students

Graphic

Setup:
In pairs, Student A is the Sage; Student B is the Scribe. Students fold a sheet of paper in half and each writes his/her name on one half.

1. The Sage gives the Scribe step-by-step instructions on how to graph problem one on a number line.

2. The Scribe records the Sage's solution step-by-step in writing on the Sage's side of the paper.

3. If the Sage is correct, the Scribe praises the Sage. Otherwise, the Scribe coaches, then praises.

4. Students switch roles for the next problem.

Chapter 3: Decimals
Lesson Two

152

ACTIVITY 2
WHERE DO YOU BELONG?

Algebraic

1. Teacher gives each student a decimal card.

2. Students mix around the room trading cards.

3. Teacher announces different inequalities for each corner of the room using Transparency 3.2.2.

4. Students look at the number on their decimal card, comparing it to each inequality.

5. Each students moves to the corner to which his/her number belongs.

6. Pairs are formed within each corner.

7. Using RallyRobin, pairs share the sum, product, or difference of the numbers on their cards, writing on paper if necessary.

8. Students trade cards with someone in their corner.

9. Repeat steps 2–8 with the next set of inequalities on the transparency.

Note: During the corner phase, students could line up in numerical order; get in groups of three and find the sum, product, or difference of the numbers; or state to which set(s) the number(s) belong. This is an excellent opportunity for reviewing concepts.

▶ **Structure**
· Corners

▶ **Materials**
· Decimal Cards (Blackline 3.1.5)
· Transparency 3.2.2
· 1 sheet of paper and pencil per pair of students

ACTIVITY 3
EVALUATE MY EXPRESSION

Algebraic

Setup:
In pairs, Student A is the Sage; Student B is the Scribe. Students fold a sheet of paper in half and each writes his/her name on one half.

1. The Sage gives the Scribe step-by-step instructions on how to evaluate problem one.

2. The Scribe records the Sage's solution step-by-step in writing on the Sage's side of the paper.

3. If the Sage is correct, the Scribe praises the Sage. Otherwise, the Scribe coaches, then praises.

4. Students switch roles for the next problem.

▶ **Structure**
· Sage-N-Scribe

▶ **Materials**
· Transparency 3.2.3
· 1 sheet of paper and pencil per pair of students

Chapter 3: Decimals
Lesson Two

ACTIVITY

4

SIMPLIFY MY EXPRESSION

▶ **Structure**
• Sage-N-Scribe

▶ **Materials**
• Transparency 3.2.4
• 1 sheet of paper and pencil per pair of students

Algebraic

Setup:
In pairs, Student A is the Sage; Student B is the Scribe. Students fold a sheet of paper in half and each writes his/her name on one half.

1. The Sage gives the Scribe step-by-step instructions on how to simplify problem one.

2. The Scribe records the Sage's solution step-by-step in writing on the Sage's side of the paper.

3. If the Sage is correct, the Scribe praises the Sage. Otherwise, the Scribe coaches, then praises.

4. Students switch roles for the next problem.

ACTIVITY

5

GEOMETRIC APPLICATIONS

▶ **Structure**
• Sage-N-Scribe

▶ **Materials**
• Blacklines 3.2.5 and 1.2.11 per pair of students
• 1 sheet of paper and pencil per pair of students

Algebraic

Setup:
In pairs, Student A is the Sage; Student B is the Scribe. Students fold a sheet of paper in half and each writes his/her name on one half.

1. The Sage gives the Scribe step-by-step instructions on how to solve problem one.

2. The Scribe records the Sage's solution step-by-step in writing on the Sage's side of the paper.

3. If the Sage is correct, the Scribe praises the Sage. Otherwise, the Scribe coaches, then praises.

4. Students switch roles for the next problem.

Cooperative Learning and Pre-Algebra: Becky Bride
Kagan Publishing • 1 (800) 933-2667 • www.KaganOnline.com

WHAT DID WE LEARN?

Synthesis

1. Each teammate signs his/her name in the upper right corner of the team paper with the colored pen/pencil he/she is using.

2. One teammate writes "*Decimal Expressions*" in the center of the team paper in a rectangle.

3. Teammate 1 shares with the team one core concept he/she learned in the unit.

4. The student checks for consensus.

5. The teammates show agreement or lack of agreement with thumbs up or down.

6. If there is agreement, the students celebrate and the teammate records the core concept on the graphic organizer, connecting it with a line to the main idea, *Decimal Expressions*. If not, teammates discuss the response until there is agreement and then they celebrate.

7. Play continues with the next student's core concept, until all core concepts are exhausted.

8. Repeat steps 3–7 with teammates adding details to each core concept and making bridges between related ideas.

▶ **Structure**
• RoundTable Consensus

▶ **Materials**
• 1 large sheet of paper per team
• 1 different colored pen or pencil for each student in the team

ACTIVITY 1 GRAPH MY INEQUALITY

Structure: Sage-N-Scribe

Graph each of the following on a number line.

1. $x > 3.7$

2. $-2.5 \geq y$

3. $-10.7 < n$

4. $m < 12.8$

5. $30.5 \geq g$

6. $-23.4 \leq w$

7. $d < (-44.9)$

8. $h > 56.2$

Answers will vary.

Cooperative Learning and Pre-Algebra: Becky Bride
Kagan Publishing • 1 (800) 933-2667 • www.KaganOnline.com

ACTIVITY

2 **WHERE DO YOU BELONG?**

DECIMALS
3.6

Structure: Corners

Listen to the teacher for instructions.

Round 1:

$x \leq (-5.9)$ $-5.9 < x \leq 1.3$

$1.3 < x < 4.2$ $4.2 \leq x$

Round 2:

$x < (-4.8)$ $-4.8 \leq x < (-1)$

$-1 \leq x \leq 2$ $x > 2$

Round 3:

$x \leq (-5.09)$ $-5.09 < x \leq (-0.803)$

$-0.803 < x < 3.607$ $x \geq 3.607$

ACTIVITY 3

EVALUATE MY EXPRESSION

DECIMALS **3.6**

Structure: Sage-N-Scribe

Evaluate each of the following if $x = (-0.2)$, $h = 1.5$, $w = (-5)$, and $m = 3.2$.

1. $3x - w^2$

2. $2hm - x$

3. $\dfrac{4h}{w} - m$

4. $h(x^2 - m)$

5. $-m - (w - x^2)$

6. $\dfrac{2m}{x} - 0.3h$

7. $2w - x + h$

8. $-x - (m + w)^2$

Answers:

1. –25.6	2. 9.8	3. –4.4	4. –4.74
5. 1.84	6. –32.45	7. –8.3	8. –3.04

Cooperative Learning and Pre-Algebra: Becky Bride
Kagan Publishing • 1 (800) 933-2667 • www.KaganOnline.com

ACTIVITY 4 SIMPLIFY MY EXPRESSION

DECIMALS 3.6

Structure: Sage-N-Scribe

Simplify each expression.

1. $3.7x^2 - 0.7y + (0.2x)^2$

2. $-w - 1.8d + 4 + 0.4w$

3. $-12.3xy - 7.3x + 9.8xy$

4. $(-p)^2 - 5.1p^2 + 0.3$

5. $7.2x - 0.15xy - (-y) - 2.7x + 6.1y$

6. $-2^2 - 4.6w + 11.7w + (-0.2)^3$

7. $-6.31h - 3^3 + 5.03h - (-2)^2$

8. $16.8n^2 - 3.2n - (-1.1n)^2$

Answers:
1. $3.74x^2 - 0.7y$ 2. $-0.6w - 1.8d + 4$ 3. $-2.5xy - 7.3x$
4. $-4.1p^2 + 0.3$ 5. $4.5x - 0.15xy + 7.1y$ 6. $-4.008 + 7.1w$
7. $-1.28h - 13$ 8. $15.59n^2 - 3.2n$

ACTIVITY

5

GEOMETRIC APPLICATIONS

Structure: Sage-N-Scribe

Solve each problem. Round answers to the nearest hundredth. Use 3.14 for π.

1. Find the volume of a spherical balloon whose radius is 3 inches.

2. Treats R Us bakery delivers baked goods in a five mile radius from their store. What is the area of their delivery region?

3. Brian is building a rectangular driveway whose dimensions will be 10 yards by 8.3 yards by 0.75 yards. How many cubic yards of concrete is needed to make his driveway? If each cubic yard of concrete costs $70.50, how much will the driveway cost?

4. A cylindrical water storage facility is twenty feet tall and has a fifty foot diameter. If there are 7.48 gallons of water in 1 cubic foot, how many gallons of water will the facility hold? If water is pumped into the facility at a rate of sixteen gallons a minute, how long will it take to fill the storage tank? Round your answer to a) nearest minute, and b) nearest hour.

5. What is the measure of one interior angle of an equiangular polygon with thirteen sides?

Cooperative Learning and Pre-Algebra: Becky Bride
Kagan Publishing • 1 (800) 933-2667 • www.KaganOnline.com

GEOMETRIC APPLICATIONS

ACTIVITY 5

Structure: Sage-N-Scribe

6. How many feet of fencing are required to fence a rectangular garden whose dimensions are 12.7 feet by 9.4 feet?

7. Payal is making a circular tablecloth whose radius is 3.4 feet. How many feet of fringe is needed to go around the edge of the tablecloth? How much will the fringe cost if its price is $1.33 per foot?

8. An ice cream cone has a radius of 1.5 inches and a height of 3.5 inches. Sam puts a spherical scoop of ice cream whose radius is 1. 5 inches on top of the cone. If the ice cream melts, will it fit in the cone?

Answers:
1. 113.04 in.³
2. 78.5 mi²
3. 62.25 yd³; $4,388.63
4. 239,590 gal., 18,349 minutes; 306 hours
5. 152.31 degrees
6. 44.20 ft
7. 21.35 ft; $28.40
8. cone: 8.24 in.³; ice cream: 14.13 in.³; no

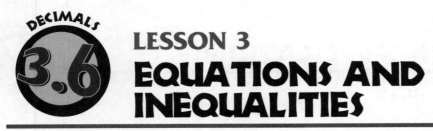

LESSON 3
EQUATIONS AND INEQUALITIES

This lesson has students solve one- and two-step equations and inequalities whose constants and coefficients are rational numbers, with at least one decimal place. The algebra is reinforced, along with working with decimals. Each activity asks students to graph their answer, reinforcing graphing of solutions, equations, and inequalities, and the graphing of decimals. The lesson also has application problems that require students to write and solve equations or inequalities. The last activity has students synthesize all they have learned in the decimal unit.

ACTIVITY 1
SOLVE MY ONE-STEP EQUATION

▶ **Structure**
•Sage-N-Scribe

▶ **Materials**
•Transparency 3.3.1
• 1 sheet of paper and pencil per pair of students

Algebraic/Graphic

Setup:
In pairs, Student A is the Sage; Student B is the Scribe. Students fold a sheet of paper in half and each writes his/her name on one half.

1. The Sage gives the Scribe step-by-step instructions on how to solve and graph problem one.

2. The Scribe records the Sage's solution step-by-step in writing on the Sage's side of the paper.

3. If the Sage is correct, the Scribe praises the Sage. Otherwise, the Scribe coaches, then praises.

4. Students switch roles for the next problem.

ACTIVITY 2
SOLVE MY TWO-STEP EQUATION

▶ **Structure**
•Sage-N-Scribe

▶ **Materials**
•Transparency 3.3.2
• 1 sheet of paper and pencil per pair of students

Algebraic/Graphic

Setup:
In pairs, Student A is the Sage; Student B is the Scribe. Students fold a sheet of paper in half and each writes his/her name on one half.

1. The Sage gives the Scribe step-by-step instructions on how to solve and graph problem one.

2. The Scribe records the Sage's solution step-by-step in writing on the Sage's side of the paper.

3. If the Sage is correct, the Scribe praises the Sage. Otherwise, the Scribe coaches, then praises.

4. Students switch roles for the next problem.

Cooperative Learning and Pre-Algebra: Becky Bride
Kagan Publishing • 1 (800) 933-2667 • www.KaganOnline.com

ACTIVITY
3

SOLVE MY ONE-STEP INEQUALITY

Algebraic/Graphic

Setup:
In pairs, Student A is the Sage; Student B is the Scribe. Students fold a sheet of paper in half and each writes his/her name on one half.

1. The Sage gives the Scribe step-by-step instructions on how to solve and graph problem one.

2. The Scribe records the Sage's solution step-by-step in writing on the Sage's side of the paper.

3. If the Sage is correct, the Scribe praises the Sage. Otherwise, the Scribe coaches, then praises.

4. Students switch roles for the next problem.

▶ **Structure**
•Sage-N-Scribe

▶ **Materials**
•Transparency 3.3.3
•1 sheet of paper and pencil per pair of students

ACTIVITY
4

SOLVE MY TWO-STEP INEQUALITY

Algebraic/Graphic

Setup:
In pairs, Student A is the Sage; Student B is the Scribe. Students fold a sheet of paper in half and each writes his/her name on one half.

1. The Sage gives the Scribe step-by-step instructions on how to solve and graph problem one.

2. The Scribe records the Sage's solution step-by-step in writing on the Sage's side of the paper.

3. If the Sage is correct, the Scribe praises the Sage. Otherwise, the Scribe coaches, then praises.

4. Students switch roles for the next problem.

▶ **Structure**
•Sage-N-Scribe

▶ **Materials**
•Transparency 3.3.4
•1 sheet of paper and pencil per pair of students

APPLY ME

▶ **Structure**
• Sage-N-Scribe

▶ **Materials**
• Blacklines 3.3.5 and 1.2.11 per pair of students
• 1 sheet of paper and pencil per pair of students

Algebraic

Setup:
In pairs, Student A is the Sage; Student B is the Scribe. Students fold a sheet of paper in half and each writes his/her name on one half.

1. The Sage gives the Scribe step-by-step instructions on how to solve problem one.

2. The Scribe records the Sage's solution step-by-step in writing on the Sage's side of the paper.

3. If the Sage is correct, the Scribe praises the Sage. Otherwise, the Scribe coaches, then praises.

4. Students switch roles for the next problem.

WHAT DID WE LEARN?

▶ **Structure**
• RoundTable Consensus

▶ **Materials**
• 1 large sheet of paper per team
• 1 different color pen or pencil for each student in the team

Synthesis

1. Each teammate signs his/her name in the upper right corner of the team paper with the colored pen/pencil he/she is using.

2. One teammate writes "*Decimal Equations and Inequalities*" in the center of the team paper in a rectangle.

3. Teammate 1 shares with the team one core concept he/she learned in the entire unit.

4. The student checks for consensus.

5. The teammates show agreement or lack of agreement with thumbs up or down.

6. If there is agreement, the students celebrate and the teammate records the core concept on the graphic organizer, connecting it with a line to the main idea, *Decimal Equations and Inequalities*. If not, teammates discuss the response until there is agreement and then they celebrate.

7. Play continues with the next student's core concept, until all core concepts are exhausted.

8. Repeat steps 3–7 with teammates adding details to each core concept and making bridges between related ideas.

Cooperative Learning and Pre-Algebra: Becky Bride
Kagan Publishing • 1 (800) 933-2667 • www.KaganOnline.com

SOLVE MY ONE-STEP EQUATION

Structure: Sage-N-Scribe

Solve each equation and graph the answer on a number line. Round each answer to the hundredths place.

1. $0.3x = 15$

2. $\dfrac{x}{1.4} = (-0.2)$

3. $h - 3.7 = (-12)$

4. $-0.048 + u = 1.7$

5. $\dfrac{n}{-0.4} = (-1.5)$

6. $g + 1.13 = 0.4$

7. $-1.003 + w = (-2.4)$

8. $-1.03m = (-.05)$

Answers:

1. 50	2. −0.28	3. −8.3	4. 1.75
5. 0.6	6. −0.73	7. −1.40	8. 0.05

SOLVE MY TWO-STEP EQUATION

Structure: Sage-N-Scribe

Solve each equation and graph the answer on a number line. Round each answer to the hundredths place.

1. $-3x - 0.8 = 4.9$

2. $2.8 - 0.3m = 5$

3. $19.1 = 3.1y + 7.2$

4. $0.34 = (-1.53) - 4h$

5. $-1.81 = 0.5w + 3.07$

6. $5.1 - 7p = (-9.9)$

7. $\dfrac{-d}{0.6} - 14.5 = (-6.8)$

8. $18.9 = 4.21 - \dfrac{k}{0.3}$

Answers:
1. −1.9	2. −7.33	3. 3.84	4. −0.47
5. −9.76	6. 2.14	7. −4.62	8. −4.41

Cooperative Learning and Pre-Algebra: Becky Bride
Kagan Publishing • 1 (800) 933-2667 • www.KaganOnline.com

SOLVE MY ONE-STEP INEQUALITY

DECIMALS
3.6

Structure: Sage-N-Scribe

Solve each inequality and graph the answer on a number line. Round answers to the nearest hundredth.

1. $h - 21.7 > 3.02$

2. $(-0.4g) < (-5.9)$

3. $\dfrac{w}{-5} \geq 0.3$

4. $9.3 \leq k + 12.7$

5. $12 < d + 9.8$

6. $16.4 > 2x$

7. $(-3.2) \leq (-4u)$

8. $m - 2.91 \geq (-3)$

Answers:

1. $h > 24.72$	2. $g > 14.75$	3. $w \leq (-1.5)$	4. $k \geq (-3.4)$
5. $d > 2.2$	6. $x < 8.2$	7. $u \leq 0.8$	8. $m \geq (-0.09)$

SOLVE MY TWO-STEP INEQUALITY

Structure: Sage-N-Scribe

Solve each inequality and graph the answer on a number line. Round answers to the nearest hundredth.

1. $2.1x - 3.7 > 5.9$

2. $(-0.7)h + 2.3 \leq 7$

3. $8.3 \leq 5m + 1.6$

4. $(-4.1) \geq 0.8x + 10$

5. $(-16.3) > 9 - 1.8n$

6. $20.1 < 6.7w - 3$

7. $42.3 - 6k \geq 6.3$

8. $17.9 - 0.2y \geq 4.6$

Answers:
1. $x > 4.57$ 2. $h \geq (-6.71)$ 3. $m \geq 1.34$ 4. $x \leq (-17.63)$
5. $n > 14.06$ 6. $w > 3.45$ 7. $k \leq 6$ 8. $y \leq 66.5$

Cooperative Learning and Pre-Algebra: Becky Bride
Kagan Publishing • 1 (800) 933-2667 • www.KaganOnline.com

5 APPLY ME

Structure: Sage-N-Scribe

Write and solve an equation or inequality for each problem. Use 3.14 for π.

1. Dustin wants to fence in a rectangular area for his dogs to safely play. If the length of the dog run is 15.6 feet and the area is to be 120 square feet, how wide must the dog run be? Round to the nearest hundredths place.

2. Candace has $120 to spend. If she buys three shirts at $9.99 each, what are the possible number of skirts she can buy if each skirt is $14.99? Round to the nearest whole number.

3. Alan earns $7.50 per hour. Find the number of possible hours he must work to make at least $250. Round to the nearest hundredths place.

4. José is making a circular tablecloth and is going to use braid around the edge that is priced by the foot. The diameter of the tablecloth is 8 feet. If the total cost of the braid is $29.89 (before tax), what is the price of the braid per foot? Round to the nearest hundredths place.

5. Kathy bought food for her horse. She bought 12 pounds of grain at $6.89 per pound. She also bought hay. If the total cost of the feed was $176.22, and each bale of hay cost $15.59, find the number of bales of hay she bought.

6. A person can pick 2.5 bushels of oranges in an hour. If five people are picking oranges, how long will it take to pick 68 bushels? Round to the nearest hundredths place.

Answers:
1. $15.6w = 120$; 7.69 ft
3. $7.50h \geq 250$; at least 33.33 hr
5. $82.68 + 15.59h = 176.22$; 6 bales

2. $120 \geq 29.97 + 14.99k$; 0 to 6 skirts
4. $29.89 = 25.12p$; $1.19 per ft
6. $12.5h = 68$; 5.44 hr

FRACTIONS

This chapter works with fractions. Lesson 1 is all about number sense. Subsets of the real numbers are reviewed, with the incorporation of fractions. Equivalent forms, ordering, comparing, and operations on fractions should be similar to what students have learned in previous years. To reinforce rules of signed numbers, the students work with both positive and negative fractions. Graphing, exponents, and order of operations are also reviewed using fractional numbers. Lesson 2 reinforces evaluating and simplifying expressions and graphing inequalities using fractional coefficients and constants. Lesson 3 reinforces solving equations and inequalities whose coefficients and constants are fractions. The chapter ends with a geometric application activity and a synthesis activity.

LESSON 1 NUMBER SENSE

ACTIVITY 1: Classify Me
ACTIVITY 2: Write an Equivalent Fraction
ACTIVITY 3: Write an Equivalent Decimal
ACTIVITY 4: Write Equivalent Forms—Take 2
ACTIVITY 5: Find a Fraction Between Us
ACTIVITY 6: Compare Me
ACTIVITY 7: Mix It Up
ACTIVITY 8: Graph Me Twice
ACTIVITY 9: Plot My Point
ACTIVITY 10: Expand Me
ACTIVITY 11: Rewrite Me Using Exponents
ACTIVITY 12: Evaluate Me
ACTIVITY 13: Multiply Me
ACTIVITY 14: Divide Me
ACTIVITY 15: Order of Operations
ACTIVITY 16: Order of Operations—Take 2
ACTIVITY 17: Applications
ACTIVITY 18: What Did We Learn?

LESSON 2 EXPRESSIONS

ACTIVITY 1: Rewrite My Coefficient
ACTIVITY 2: Adjust My Negative Sign
ACTIVITY 3: Graph My Inequality
ACTIVITY 4: Where Do You Belong?
ACTIVITY 5: Evaluate My Expression
ACTIVITY 6: Evaluate Me Simultaneously
ACTIVITY 7: Simplify My Expression
ACTIVITY 8: Write Me Using Symbols
ACTIVITY 9: What Did We Learn?

LESSON 3 EQUATIONS AND INEQUALITIES

ACTIVITY 1: Solve My One-Step Equation
ACTIVITY 2: Solve My Two-Step Equation
ACTIVITY 3: Solve My One-Step Inequality
ACTIVITY 4: Solve My Two-Step Inequality
ACTIVITY 5: Geometric Applications
ACTIVITY 6: What Did We Learn?

LESSON 1
NUMBER SENSE

This lesson reinforces many topics that began in the whole number chapter. Students will classify numbers involving fractions according to the subset(s) of the real numbers to which they belong. The next several activities link fractions to decimals and have students write equivalent forms. Activity 5 has students use equivalent forms of fractions to find a fraction between two other fractions. Activities 6 and 7 have students order and compare fractions. Activities 8 and 9 reinforces graphing on a number line and coordinate plane since students have to graph fractional numbers. Exponents are revisited in activities 10 and 11. The four basic arithmetic operations are practiced in activities 12 through 14 by using positive and negative fractions. Order of operations is reinforced in activities 15 and 16 as students solve problems with fractions. Finally, the lesson ends with an application activity.

ACTIVITY

1 CLASSIFY ME

▶ **Structure**
· RallyCoach

▶ **Materials**
· Transparency 4.1.1
· 1 sheet of paper and pencil per pair of students

Numeric

1. Teacher poses many problems using Transparency 4.1.1.

2. Partner A classifies the number in problem one as a natural, whole, integer, rational, and/or real number, writing his/her response on the paper.

3. Partner B watches, listens, checks, and praises.

4. Partner B repeats step 2 for the next problem.

5. Partner A watches, listens, checks, and praises.

6. Repeat for remaining problems starting at step 2.

ACTIVITY

2 WRITE AN EQUIVALENT FRACTION

▶ **Structure**
· RallyCoach

▶ **Materials**
· Transparency 4.1.2
· 1 sheet of paper and pencil per pair of students

Numeric

1. Teacher poses many problems using Transparency 4.1.2.

2. Partner A writes a fraction equivalent to the fraction in problem one on the paper.

3. Partner B watches, listens, checks, and praises.

4. Partner B writes an equivalent fraction for the same problem on the paper.

5. Partner A watches, listens, checks, and praises.

6. Repeat for remaining problems starting at step 2.

Cooperative Learning and Pre-Algebra: Becky Bride
Kagan Publishing • 1 (800) 933-2667 • www.KaganOnline.com

ACTIVITY

3 WRITE AN EQUIVALENT DECIMAL

Numeric

1. Teacher poses many problems using Transparency 4.1.2.

2. Partner A writes a decimal equivalent to the fraction in problem one on the paper.

3. Partner B watches, listens, checks, and praises.

4. Partner B writes an equivalent decimal for the next problem on the paper.

5. Partner A watches, listens, checks, and praises.

6. Repeat for remaining problems starting at step 2.

▶ **Structure**
• RallyCoach

▶ **Materials**
• Transparency 4.1.2
• 1 sheet of paper and pencil per pair of students

ACTIVITY

4 WRITE EQUIVALENT FORMS—TAKE 2

Numeric

1. Teacher poses many problems using Transparency 4.1.3.

2. Partner A writes a fraction equivalent to the decimal in problem one on the paper.

3. Partner B watches, listens, checks, and praises.

4. Partner B writes an equivalent fraction for the next problem on the paper.

5. Partner A watches, listens, checks, and praises.

6. Repeat for remaining problems starting at step 2.

▶ **Structure**
• RallyCoach

▶ **Materials**
• Transparency 4.1.3
• 1 sheet of paper and pencil per pair of students

ACTIVITY

5 FIND A FRACTION BETWEEN US

Numeric

1. Teacher poses many problems using Transparency 4.1.4.

2. Partner A writes a fraction that is between the two fractions in problem one on the paper.

3. Partner B watches, listens, checks, and praises.

4. Partner B writes a fraction between the two fractions for the next problem on the paper.

5. Partner A watches, listens, checks, and praises.

6. Repeat for remaining problems starting at step 2.

▶ **Structure**
• RallyCoach

▶ **Materials**
• Transparency 4.1.4
• 1 sheet of paper and pencil per pair of students

ACTIVITY

6 COMPARE ME

▶ **Structure**
• RallyCoach

▶ **Materials**
• Transparency 4.1.5
• 1 sheet of paper and pencil per pair of students

In addition to writing a correct mathematical inequality, this activity also asks the students to write two sentences—one reading the expression from left to right, then the other one reading the expression from right to left.

Numeric

1. Teacher poses many problems using Transparency 4.1.5.

2. Partner A compares the two numbers and writes the problem, inserting the correct inequality symbol. Then he/she writes the expression as a

sentence as the inequality would be read from left to right. He/she writes a second sentence as the inequality would be read from right to left.

3. Partner B watches, listens, checks, and praises.

4. Partner B repeats step 2 for the next problem.

5. Partner A watches, listens, checks, and praises.

6. Repeat for remaining problems starting at step 2.

ACTIVITY

7 MIX IT UP

▶ **Structure:**
• Quiz-Quiz-Trade

▶ **Materials**
• 1 set of Fraction Cards (Blackline 4.1.6)
• 1 sheet of paper and pencil per student

Numeric

Setup:
The cards need to be copied onto cardstock and cut into individual cards. Cards are distributed to the students, 1 card per student.

1. StandUp–HandUp–PairUp.

2. Partner A quizzes his/her partner, asking which fraction on the two cards is larger.

3. Partner B answers, writing his/her answer on his/her paper.

4. Partner A praises or coaches.

5. Partner B quizzes his/her partner, asking for a fraction that is between the two fractions on the cards.

6. Partner A answers, writing his/her answer on his/her paper.

7. Partner B praises or coaches.

8. Partners trade cards.

9. Repeat steps 1–8 as many times as the teacher chooses. The questions may change. Students could ask each other to find the decimal that is equivalent to the fraction on his/her card. Students could ask each other to what subset(s) of the real numbers the other's fraction belongs. These cards could be mixed with the decimal cards and/or integer cards to add new dimension to the activity. These cards can be re-used after the 4 basic operations are reviewed. The students could ask each other the sum, difference, quotient, or product of the two numbers. At the end of the activity, the class could be asked to line up in numerical order.

Cooperative Learning and Pre-Algebra: Becky Bride
Kagan Publishing • 1 (800) 933-2667 • www.KaganOnline.com

ACTIVITY

8 GRAPH ME TWICE

Graphic

1. Teacher poses many problems using Transparency 4.1.7.

2. Partner A graphs the number in the first problem on a number line, using any scale he/she chooses.

3. Partner B watches, listens, checks, and praises.

4. Partner B graphs the same number on a different number line, using a different scale of his/her choice.

5. Partner A watches, listens, checks, and praises.

6. Repeat for remaining problems starting at step 2.

▶ **Structure**
• RallyCoach

▶ **Materials**
• Transparency 4.1.7
• 1 sheet of paper, pencil, and ruler per pair of students

ACTIVITY

9 PLOT MY POINT

Graphic

1. Teacher poses many problems using Transparency 4.1.8.

2. Partner A plots the point in the first problem on a coordinate plane, using any scale he/she chooses for each axis that will work well for both denominators.

3. Partner B watches, listens, checks, and praises.

4. Partner B plots the point in the next problem on a coordinate plane, using any scale he/she chooses for each axis that will work well for both denominators.

5. Partner A watches, listens, checks, and praises.

6. Repeat for remaining problems starting at step 2.

▶ **Structure**
• RallyCoach

▶ **Materials**
• Transparency 4.1.8
• 1-2 sheets of graph paper, pencil, and ruler per pair of students

ACTIVITY

10 EXPAND ME

▶ **Structure**
• RallyCoach

▶ **Materials**
• Transparency 4.1.9
• 1 sheet of paper and pencil per pair of students

Numeric

1. Teacher poses many problems using Transparency 4.1.9.

2. Partner A expands the expression in problem one using multiplication, writing his/her response on the paper.

3. Partner B watches, listens, checks, and praises.

4. Partner B expands the expression in the next problem, writing his/her response on the paper.

5. Partner A watches, listens, checks, and praises.

6. Repeat for remaining problems starting at step 2.

ACTIVITY

11 REWRITE ME USING EXPONENTS

▶ **Structure**
• RallyCoach

▶ **Materials**
• Transparency 4.1.10
• 1 sheet of paper and pencil per pair of students

Numeric

1. Teacher poses many problems using Transparency 4.1.10.

2. Partner A rewrites the expression in problem one using exponents, writing his/her response on the paper.

3. Partner B watches, listens, checks, and praises.

4. Partner B rewrites the expression in the next problem, writing his/her response on the paper.

5. Partner A watches, listens, checks, and praises.

6. Repeat for remaining problems starting at step 2.

Cooperative Learning and Pre-Algebra: Becky Bride
Kagan Publishing • 1 (800) 933-2667 • www.KaganOnline.com

ACTIVITY

12 EVALUATE ME

Numeric

Setup:
In pairs, Student A is the Sage; Student B is the Scribe. Students fold a sheet of paper in half and each writes his/her name on one half.

1. The Sage gives the Scribe step-by-step instructions on how to evaluate problem one.

2. The Scribe records the Sage's solution step-by-step in writing on the Sage's side of the paper.

3. If the Sage is correct, the Scribe praises the Sage. Otherwise, the Scribe coaches, then praises.

4. Students switch roles for the next problem.

▶ **Structure**
•Sage-N-Scribe

▶ **Materials**
•Transparency 4.1.11
• 1 sheet of paper and pencil per pair of students

ACTIVITY

13 MULTIPLY ME

Numeric

Setup:
In pairs, Student A is the Sage; Student B is the Scribe. Students fold a sheet of paper in half and each writes his/her name on one half.

1. The Sage gives the Scribe step-by-step instructions on how to multiply the numbers in problem one.

2. The Scribe records the Sage's solution step-by-step in writing on the Sage's side of the paper.

3. If the Sage is correct, the Scribe praises the Sage. Otherwise, the Scribe coaches, then praises.

4. Students switch roles for the next problem.

▶ **Structure**
•Sage-N-Scribe

▶ **Materials**
•Transparency 4.1.12
• 1 sheet of paper and pencil per pair of students

ACTIVITY
14 DIVIDE ME

▶ **Structure**
• Sage-N-Scribe

▶ **Materials**
• Transparency 4.1.13
• 1 sheet of paper and pencil per pair of students

Numeric

Setup:
In pairs, Student A is the Sage; Student B is the Scribe. Students fold a sheet of paper in half and each writes his/her name on one half.

1. The Sage gives the Scribe step-by-step instructions on how to divide the numbers in problem one.

2. The Scribe records the Sage's solution step-by-step in writing on the Sage's side of the paper.

3. If the Sage is correct, the Scribe praises the Sage. Otherwise, the Scribe coaches, then praises.

4. Students switch roles for the next problem.

ACTIVITY
15 ORDER OF OPERATIONS

▶ **Structure**
• Sage-N-Scribe

▶ **Materials**
• Transparency 4.1.14
• 1 sheet of paper and pencil per pair of students

Numeric

Setup:
In pairs, Student A is the Sage; Student B is the Scribe. Students fold a sheet of paper in half and each writes his/her name on one half.

1. The Sage gives the Scribe step-by-step instructions on how to solve problem one.

2. The Scribe records the Sage's solution step-by-step in writing on the Sage's side of the paper.

3. If the Sage is correct, the Scribe praises the Sage. Otherwise, the Scribe coaches, then praises.

4. Students switch roles for the next problem.

Cooperative Learning and Pre-Algebra: Becky Bride
Kagan Publishing • 1 (800) 933-2667 • www.KaganOnline.com

ACTIVITY

16 ORDER OF OPERATIONS—TAKE 2

Numeric

Setup:
The operation cards need to be copied onto cardstock and cut into individual cards. Teacher gives each team a set of fraction cards and a set of operation cards. The team separates the fraction cards from the operation cards, mixes each stack, and places each stack facedown.

1. The teacher selects one student on each team to be the Showdown Captain for the first round.

2. The Showdown Captain draws 3 fraction cards and 2 operation cards. He/she arranges the cards to form an arithmetic expression. The captain asks each teammate to evaluate the expression and provides think time.

3. Working alone, all students, including the Showdown Captain, evaluate the expression.

4. When finished, teammates signal they're ready.

5. The Showdown Captain calls, "Showdown."

6. Teammates show and discuss their answers. The Showdown Captain leads the checking.

7. If correct, the team celebrates; if not, teammates tutor, then celebrate.

8. The person on the left of the Showdown Captain becomes the new Showdown Captain for the next round.

9. Repeat steps 2–8.

▶ **Structure**
•Showdown

▶ **Materials**
• 1 set of Fraction Cards (Blackline 4.1.6) and 1 set of Operation Cards (Blackline 4.1.15) per team
• 1 sheet of paper and pencil per pair

Tips:
Use different colored cardstock for the expression cards and operation cards for easy sorting. The cards can be chosen faceup or facedown. To vary the activity, you could mix in some integer, whole number, and/or decimal cards with the fraction cards.

ACTIVITY

17 APPLICATIONS

Numeric

Setup:
In pairs, Student A is the Sage; Student B is the Scribe. Students fold a sheet of paper in half and each writes his/her name on one half.

1. The Sage gives the Scribe step-by-step instructions on how to solve problem one.

2. The Scribe records the Sage's solution step-by-step in writing on the Sage's side of the paper.

3. If the Sage is correct, the Scribe praises the Sage. Otherwise, the Scribe coaches, then praises.

4. Students switch roles for the next problem.

▶ **Structure**
•Sage-N-Scribe

▶ **Materials**
•Blackline 4.1.16
• 1 sheet of paper and pencil per pair of students

WHAT DID WE LEARN?

▶ **Structure**
  • RoundTable Consensus

▶ **Materials**
  • 1 large sheet of paper per team
  • 1 different colored pen or pencil for each student in the team

Synthesis

1. Each teammate signs his/her name in the upper right corner of the team paper with the colored pen/pencil he/she is using.

2. One teammate writes *"Fractions"* in the center of the team paper in a rectangle.

3. Teammate 1 shares with the team one core concept he/she learned in the unit.

4. The student checks for consensus.

5. The teammates show agreement or lack of agreement with thumbs up or down.

6. If there is agreement, the students celebrate and the teammate records the core concept on the graphic organizer, connecting it with a line to the main idea, *Integers.* If not, teammates discuss the response until there is agreement and then they celebrate.

7. Play continues with the next student's core concept, until all core concepts are exhausted.

8. Repeat steps 3–7 with teammates adding details to each core concept and making bridges between related ideas.

Cooperative Learning and Pre-Algebra: Becky Bride
Kagan Publishing • 1 (800) 933-2667 • www.KaganOnline.com

ACTIVITY

1 CLASSIFY ME

Structure: RallyCoach

Classify each number by stating the set(s) of numbers to which it belongs.

1. $\dfrac{-2}{3}$

2. $\dfrac{10}{2}$

3. 0.7

4. $1\dfrac{5}{7}$

5. $\dfrac{24}{8}$

6. $\dfrac{0}{9}$

7. $\dfrac{5}{0}$

8. -1.5

9. $-\dfrac{20}{4}$

10. $-\dfrac{15}{9}$

Answers:
1. rational, real
2. natural, whole, integer, rational, real
3. rational, real
4. rational, real
5. natural, whole, integer, rational, real
6. whole, integer, rational, real,
7. not real
8. rational, real
9. integer, rational, real
10. rational, real

2&3 WRITE AN EQUIVALENT FRACTION
WRITE AN EQUIVALENT DECIMAL

Structure: RallyCoach

Directions:
Activity 2: Write an equivalent fraction.
Activity 3: Write an equivalent decimal.
Round to the thousandths place.

1. $\dfrac{-2}{3}$ 2. $\dfrac{16}{6}$ 3. $\dfrac{-7}{4}$

4. $\dfrac{3}{5}$ 5. $\dfrac{10}{12}$ 6. -4

7. 7 8. $-\dfrac{15}{21}$ 9. $\dfrac{-16}{14}$

10. $\dfrac{8}{5}$ 11. $\dfrac{4}{9}$ 12. $-\dfrac{24}{18}$

Answers:
Activity 2: Answers will vary.

Activity 3

1. −0.667	2. 2.667	3. −1.75	4. 0.6	5. 0.833	6. −4.0
7. 7.0	8. −0.714	9. −1.143	10. 1.6	11. 0.444	12. −1.333

Cooperative Learning and Pre-Algebra: Becky Bride
Kagan Publishing • 1 (800) 933-2667 • www.KaganOnline.com

ACTIVITY
4
WRITE EQUIVALENT FORMS—TAKE 2

Structure: RallyCoach

Change each decimal into a simplified fraction.

1. 0.12   2. 4.1   3. –8.23

4. –6.82   5. 27.402   6. 15.35

7. –0.6   8. 3.072   9. 2.125

10. –0.112   11. –1.048   12. 5.8

Answers:

1. $\frac{3}{25}$ 2. $\frac{41}{10}$ 3. $\frac{-823}{100}$ 4. $\frac{-341}{50}$ 5. $\frac{13701}{500}$ 6. $\frac{307}{20}$

7. $\frac{-3}{5}$ 8. $\frac{384}{125}$ 9. $\frac{17}{8}$ 10. $\frac{-14}{125}$ 11. $\frac{-131}{125}$ 12. $\frac{29}{5}$

FIND A FRACTION BETWEEN US

Structure: RallyCoach

Find a fraction between the two given fractions

1. $\dfrac{4}{3}$, $\dfrac{4}{9}$

2. $\dfrac{-5}{12}$, $\dfrac{-5}{6}$

3. $-\dfrac{4}{9}$, $-\dfrac{7}{18}$

4. $\dfrac{1}{4}$, $\dfrac{1}{3}$

5. $\dfrac{2}{7}$, $\dfrac{1}{7}$

6. $\dfrac{5}{11}$, $\dfrac{6}{11}$

7. $-\dfrac{5}{16}$, $-\dfrac{3}{8}$

8. $-\dfrac{2}{3}$, $-\dfrac{3}{4}$

Answers will vary. Sample answers below.

1. $\dfrac{5}{9}$ 2. $\dfrac{-7}{12}$ 3. $\dfrac{-15}{36}$ 4. $\dfrac{7}{24}$

5. $\dfrac{3}{14}$ 6. $\dfrac{1}{2}$ 7. $\dfrac{-11}{32}$ 8. $\dfrac{-17}{24}$

Cooperative Learning and Pre-Algebra: Becky Bride
Kagan Publishing • 1 (800) 933-2667 • www.KaganOnline.com

ACTIVITY

6 COMPARE ME

Structure: RallyCoach

For each problem
a. Write a number sentence using the correct inequality symbol.

b. Using words, write a sentence as the inequality reads from left to right.

c. Using words, write a sentence as the inequality reads from right to left.

1. $\dfrac{4}{9}$ $\dfrac{5}{8}$

2. $-\left(\dfrac{12}{7}\right)$ $-\left(\dfrac{25}{14}\right)$

3. $-\left(\dfrac{9}{6}\right)$ $-\left(\dfrac{15}{10}\right)$

4. $\dfrac{5}{12}$ $\dfrac{3}{7}$

5. $-\left(\dfrac{14}{9}\right)$ $-\left(\dfrac{19}{12}\right)$

6. $\dfrac{12}{16}$ $\dfrac{18}{24}$

7. $\dfrac{11}{4}$ $\dfrac{23}{8}$

8. $-\left(\dfrac{11}{3}\right)$ $\dfrac{-23}{6}$

Answers:

| 1. < | 2. > | 3. = | 4. < |
| 5. > | 6. = | 7. < | 8. > |

Structure: Quiz–Quiz–Trade
Fraction Cards

$\dfrac{-24}{5}$	$\dfrac{-40}{9}$	$\dfrac{-33}{8}$	$\dfrac{-11}{3}$	$\dfrac{-27}{8}$	$\dfrac{-13}{4}$
$\dfrac{-26}{9}$	$\dfrac{-19}{7}$	$\dfrac{-29}{12}$	$\dfrac{-11}{6}$	$\dfrac{-13}{8}$	$\dfrac{-7}{5}$
$\dfrac{-8}{7}$	$\dfrac{-3}{4}$	$\dfrac{-1}{2}$	$\dfrac{-1}{3}$	$\dfrac{-1}{8}$	$\dfrac{-1}{9}$
0	$\dfrac{2}{9}$	$\dfrac{3}{8}$	$\dfrac{1}{2}$	$\dfrac{5}{6}$	$\dfrac{12}{11}$
$\dfrac{7}{6}$	$\dfrac{9}{7}$	$\dfrac{7}{4}$	$\dfrac{21}{20}$	$\dfrac{35}{16}$	$\dfrac{13}{5}$
$\dfrac{19}{7}$	$\dfrac{13}{4}$	$\dfrac{29}{8}$	$\dfrac{34}{9}$	$\dfrac{30}{7}$	$\dfrac{9}{2}$

Cooperative Learning and Pre-Algebra: Becky Bride
Kagan Publishing • 1 (800) 933-2667 • www.KaganOnline.com

ACTIVITY
8 GRAPH ME TWICE

Structure: RallyCoach

Graph each number on a number line.

1. $\dfrac{1}{3}$

2. $\dfrac{-3}{4}$

3. $-\dfrac{5}{8}$

4. $-\dfrac{5}{12}$

5. $\dfrac{11}{9}$

6. $\dfrac{22}{9}$

7. $\dfrac{-23}{9}$

8. $\dfrac{9}{5}$

Answers will vary based on scale used.

9 PLOT MY POINT

Structure: RallyCoach

Plot each point on a different coordinate plane.

1. $\left(\dfrac{5}{2}, -\dfrac{3}{4}\right)$

2. $\left(-\dfrac{2}{3}, \dfrac{14}{9}\right)$

3. $\left(-\dfrac{5}{3}, 0\right)$

4. $\left(-\dfrac{5}{6}, -\dfrac{3}{2}\right)$

5. $\left(-\dfrac{7}{8}, -\dfrac{7}{2}\right)$

6. $\left(\dfrac{9}{8}, -\dfrac{11}{6}\right)$

7. $\left(\dfrac{9}{4}, \dfrac{5}{6}\right)$

8. $\left(0, \dfrac{11}{4}\right)$

Answers will vary based on scale used for each axis.

Cooperative Learning and Pre-Algebra: Becky Bride
Kagan Publishing • 1 (800) 933-2667 • www.KaganOnline.com

ACTIVITY

10 EXPAND ME

Structure: RallyCoach

Rewrite using multiplication.

1. $\left(-\dfrac{5}{9}\right)^2$

2. $-\dfrac{4^3}{5}$

3. $\dfrac{6}{7^4}$

4. $\left(-\dfrac{1}{2}\right)^5$

5. $\dfrac{5^6}{9}$

6. $\left(\dfrac{2}{3}\right)^3$

7. $-\dfrac{2^3}{5}$

8. $-\left(\dfrac{3}{7}\right)^4$

Answers:

1. $\left(-\dfrac{5}{9}\right) \times \left(-\dfrac{5}{9}\right)$ 2. $-\dfrac{4 \times 4 \times 4}{5}$ 3. $\dfrac{6}{7 \times 7 \times 7 \times 7}$ 4. $\left(-\dfrac{1}{2}\right)\left(-\dfrac{1}{2}\right)\left(-\dfrac{1}{2}\right)\left(-\dfrac{1}{2}\right)\left(-\dfrac{1}{2}\right)$

5. $\dfrac{5 \times 5 \times 5 \times 5 \times 5 \times 5}{9}$ 6. $\left(\dfrac{2}{3}\right)\left(\dfrac{2}{3}\right)\left(\dfrac{2}{3}\right)$ 7. $-\dfrac{2 \times 2 \times 2}{5}$ 8. $-\left(\dfrac{3}{7}\right)\left(\dfrac{3}{7}\right)\left(\dfrac{3}{7}\right)\left(\dfrac{3}{7}\right)$

11 REWRITE ME USING EXPONENTS

Structure: RallyCoach

Rewrite each using exponents.

1. $\left(\dfrac{3}{4}\right)\left(\dfrac{3}{4}\right)\left(\dfrac{3}{4}\right)$

2. $\dfrac{7 \times 7 \times 7 \times 7}{5}$

3. $-\dfrac{6}{11 \times 11}$

4. $-\left(\dfrac{5}{9}\right)\left(\dfrac{5}{9}\right)\left(\dfrac{5}{9}\right)\left(\dfrac{5}{9}\right)\left(\dfrac{5}{9}\right)$

5. $-\dfrac{8 \times 8 \times 8 \times 8}{3 \times 3}$

6. $\dfrac{13}{6} \times \dfrac{13}{6} \times \dfrac{13}{6}$

7. $-\dfrac{7}{4} \times \dfrac{7}{4} \times \dfrac{7}{4} \times \dfrac{7}{4} \times \dfrac{7}{4}$

8. $-\dfrac{1}{3 \times 3}$

Answers:

1. $\left(\dfrac{3}{4}\right)^3$ 2. $\dfrac{7^4}{5}$ 3. $-\dfrac{6}{11^2}$ 4. $-\left(\dfrac{5}{9}\right)^5$

5. $-\dfrac{8^4}{3^2}$ 6. $\left(\dfrac{13}{6}\right)^3$ 7. $-\left(\dfrac{7}{4}\right)^5$ 8. $-\dfrac{1}{3^2}$

Cooperative Learning and Pre-Algebra: Becky Bride
Kagan Publishing • 1 (800) 933-2667 • www.KaganOnline.com

ACTIVITY
12 EVALUATE ME

Structure: Sage-N-Scribe

Add each of the following. Put answers in simplest form.

1. $\dfrac{5}{6} + \left(-\dfrac{5}{9}\right)$

2. $-\dfrac{2}{3} + \left(-\dfrac{13}{6}\right)$

3. $\dfrac{11}{4} + \dfrac{15}{8}$

4. $-\dfrac{11}{6} + \dfrac{3}{4}$

5. $\dfrac{5}{12} - \left(-\dfrac{2}{3}\right) - \dfrac{9}{4}$

6. $-\dfrac{9}{8} - \dfrac{11}{3} + \dfrac{5}{6}$

7. $6\dfrac{1}{2} + \left(-4\dfrac{2}{3}\right)$

8. $4\dfrac{2}{7} + \left(-1\dfrac{5}{8}\right)$

9. $2\dfrac{1}{2} - 1\dfrac{2}{3} + \dfrac{3}{4}$

10. $-5\dfrac{1}{2} - \dfrac{1}{2} + 1\dfrac{2}{3}$

Answers:

1. $\dfrac{5}{18}$ 2. $-\dfrac{17}{6} = -2\dfrac{5}{6}$ 3. $\dfrac{37}{8} = 4\dfrac{5}{8}$ 4. $-\dfrac{13}{12} = -1\dfrac{1}{12}$ 5. $-\dfrac{7}{6} = -1\dfrac{1}{6}$

6. $-\dfrac{95}{24} = -3\dfrac{23}{24}$ 7. $\dfrac{11}{6} = 1\dfrac{5}{6}$ 8. $\dfrac{149}{56} = 2\dfrac{37}{56}$ 9. $\dfrac{19}{12} = 1\dfrac{7}{12}$ 10. $\dfrac{-13}{3} = -4\dfrac{1}{3}$

ACTIVITY

13 MULTIPLY ME

Structure: Sage-N-Scribe

Multiply each of the following. Put answers in simplest form.

1. $\dfrac{4}{9}\left(-\dfrac{6}{7}\right)$

2. $-\dfrac{5}{12}\left(-\dfrac{14}{15}\right)$

3. $-\dfrac{5}{4}\left(-\dfrac{8}{9}\right)$

4. $\dfrac{12}{5}(15)$

5. $-\dfrac{2}{3}\left(-\dfrac{5}{8}\right)\left(-\dfrac{6}{7}\right)$

6. $-\dfrac{5}{9}\left(\dfrac{12}{7}\right)\left(-\dfrac{7}{15}\right)$

7. $\left(-2\dfrac{1}{3}\right)\left(1\dfrac{3}{7}\right)$

8. $\left(-1\dfrac{3}{4}\right)\left(-3\dfrac{1}{3}\right)$

9. $4\dfrac{1}{2}\times 6$

10. $-3\dfrac{1}{4}\times 1\dfrac{1}{3}$

Answers:

1. $-\dfrac{8}{21}$ 2. $\dfrac{7}{18}$ 3. $\dfrac{10}{9}=1\dfrac{1}{9}$ 4. 36 5. $-\dfrac{5}{14}$

6. $\dfrac{4}{9}$ 7. $-\dfrac{10}{3}=-3\dfrac{1}{3}$ 8. $\dfrac{35}{6}=5\dfrac{5}{6}$ 9. 27 10. $\dfrac{-13}{3}=-4\dfrac{1}{3}$

Cooperative Learning and Pre-Algebra: Becky Bride
Kagan Publishing • 1 (800) 933-2667 • www.KaganOnline.com

ACTIVITY
14 DIVIDE ME

Structure: Sage-N-Scribe

Divide each of the following.
Put answers in simplest form.

1. $-\dfrac{6}{7} \div \left(-\dfrac{3}{4}\right)$

2. $-\dfrac{1}{8} \div (-6)$

3. $9 \div \left(\dfrac{6}{7}\right)$

4. $-\dfrac{8}{9} \div (-6)$

5. $-\dfrac{5}{6} \div \left(\dfrac{15}{12}\right)$

6. $\dfrac{5}{12} \div \left(-\dfrac{3}{8}\right)$

7. $\left(1\dfrac{3}{4}\right) \div \left(-2\dfrac{2}{3}\right)$

8. $\left(-1\dfrac{3}{5}\right) \div (-4)$

9. $-\dfrac{5}{8} \div \left(-2\dfrac{5}{6}\right)$

10. $3\dfrac{1}{2} \div \left(-\dfrac{5}{3}\right)$

Answers:

1. $\dfrac{8}{7} = 1\dfrac{1}{7}$ 2. $\dfrac{1}{48}$ 3. $\dfrac{21}{2} = 10\dfrac{1}{2}$ 4. $\dfrac{4}{27}$ 5. $-\dfrac{2}{3}$

6. $-\dfrac{10}{9} = -1\dfrac{1}{9}$ 7. $-\dfrac{21}{32}$ 8. $\dfrac{2}{5}$ 9. $\dfrac{15}{68}$ 10. $-\dfrac{21}{10} = -2\dfrac{1}{10}$

ACTIVITY 15 ORDER OF OPERATIONS

Structure: Sage-N-Scribe

Evaluate each of the following. Put answers in simplest form.

1. $\dfrac{2}{3} \times \dfrac{6}{7} + \dfrac{1}{2}$

2. $-\dfrac{3}{4} - \dfrac{5}{6} \div \left(-\dfrac{2}{3}\right)$

3. $\left(-\dfrac{1}{4}\right)^2 \div \dfrac{3}{8}$

4. $\dfrac{1}{2} + \left(-\dfrac{2}{3}\right)\left(\dfrac{4}{5}\right)$

5. $-5 - \dfrac{5}{9} \div \dfrac{2}{3}$

6. $\dfrac{3}{4} - \left(-\dfrac{2}{3}\right)^2$

7. $\dfrac{4}{5} - \left(\dfrac{1}{2}\right)^2$

8. $-\dfrac{3}{8}\left(\dfrac{1}{2} + \dfrac{2}{3}\right)$

9. $-3\left(\dfrac{1}{8} - \dfrac{5}{4}\right)$

10. $-\dfrac{3}{10}\left(4 - \dfrac{2}{3}\right)$

Answers:

1. $\dfrac{15}{14} = 1\dfrac{1}{14}$ 2. $\dfrac{1}{2}$ 3. $\dfrac{1}{6}$ 4. $-\dfrac{1}{30}$ 5. $-\dfrac{35}{6} = -5\dfrac{5}{6}$

6. $\dfrac{11}{36}$ 7. $\dfrac{11}{20}$ 8. $-\dfrac{7}{16}$ 9. $\dfrac{27}{8} = 3\dfrac{3}{8}$ 10. -1

Cooperative Learning and Pre-Algebra: Becky Bride
Kagan Publishing • 1 (800) 933-2667 • www.KaganOnline.com

Blackline 4.1.15

ACTIVITY 16 ORDER OF OPERATION—TAKE 2

Structure: Showdown

Operation Cards

+	+	+	+
+	+	+	+
−	−	−	−
−	−	−	−
×	×	×	×
×	×	×	×
÷	÷	÷	÷
÷	÷	÷	÷

ACTIVITY

17 APPLICATIONS

Structure: Sage-N-Scribe

Solve each problem.

1. How many pieces of ribbon $5\frac{3}{4}$ inches long, can be cut from a ribbon that is 42 inches in length? Round to the nearest whole number.

For problems 2–3, use the recipe for fettuccine alfredo below.
   $\frac{1}{2}$ cup butter
   $\frac{3}{8}$ pound grated parmesan cheese
   1 cup heavy whipping cream
   $\frac{7}{8}$ pound fresh fettuccine noodles

2. Beth is having a dinner party and needs to triple the recipe. How much of each ingredient will she need to make the fettuccine alfredo?

3. The above recipe serves four people. Jonathon is having a friend over for dinner. How much of each ingredient will he need to use to make fettuccine alfredo for just two people?

4. Julio needs to put weed and feed on his lawn. If $2\frac{1}{2}$ ounces mixed with a gallon of water will cover 500 square feet, how many ounces of weed and feed does he need for his 4,500 square foot lawn? Round to the nearest whole number.

Cooperative Learning and Pre-Algebra: Becky Bride
Kagan Publishing • 1 (800) 933-2667 • www.KaganOnline.com

ACTIVITY

1 APPLICATIONS

Structure: Sage-N-Scribe

5. Sally is fencing her flower garden that is rectangular in shape. If the length is $3\frac{1}{2}$ feet and the width is $4\frac{3}{4}$ feet, how much fencing does she need to buy? Round to the nearest whole number.

6. Tom is making a special punch for a party. If he uses $6\frac{2}{3}$ cups of ginger ale, $2\frac{1}{2}$ cups of pineapple juice, and $3\frac{1}{4}$ cups of fruit punch, how many cups of the special punch will he have? Round to the nearest whole number.

7. A gift shop has $38\frac{3}{4}$ linear feet of wrapping paper. If $5\frac{1}{3}$ linear feet is used on Monday, $2\frac{1}{4}$ linear feet is used on Tuesday, and $7\frac{3}{8}$ linear feet is used on Wednesday, how many linear feet remain?

8. A farmer planted three fields with strawberries. One field is $5\frac{1}{3}$ acres, another is $6\frac{3}{4}$ acres, and the last one is $4\frac{5}{8}$ acres. If bunnies ate $1\frac{1}{2}$ acres of the strawberries, how many acres remain to be harvested?

Answers:

1. 7

2. $\frac{3}{2}$ c. butter, $\frac{9}{8}$ lb. cheese, 3 c. cream, $\frac{21}{8}$ lb. noodles

3. $\frac{1}{4}$ c. butter, $\frac{3}{16}$ lb. cheese, $\frac{1}{2}$ c. cream, $\frac{7}{16}$ lb. noodles

4. 23 ounces

5. 17 feet

6. 12 cups

7. 23 $\frac{19}{24}$ linear feet

8. 15 $\frac{5}{24}$ acres

LESSON 2:
EXPRESSIONS

This lesson reinforces students' understanding of algebraic expressions. The activity, Rewrite My Coefficient, has students rewrite fractional coefficients so they will understand that the fraction 2*x* divided by 3 is the same thing as 2/3 times *x*. The negative sign is in different places—numerator, denominator, or in front of the fraction. The next activity, Adjust My Negative Sign, uses the same problems as the previous activity and requires students to write equivalent coefficients with the negative sign in different places. Students will then graph inequalities on a number line that contain a fraction or mixed number. The activities that have students evaluate expressions require students to substitute fractional numbers for the variables reinforcing the arithmetic of fractions and the order of operations. Students will simplify expressions that have fractional coefficients. Finally, the students will translate algebraic expressions from words to symbols.

1 REWRITE MY COEFFICIENT

▶ **Structure**
• RallyCoach

▶ **Materials**
• Transparency 4.2.1
• 1 sheet of paper and pencil per pair of students

Algebraic

1. Teacher poses many problems using Transparency 4.2.1.

2. Partner A rewrites the coefficient in problem one so it is a fractional coefficient, writing his/her response on the paper.

3. Partner B watches, listens, checks, and praises.

4. Partner B rewrites the coefficient in the next problem so it is a fractional coefficient, writing his/her response on the paper.

5. Partner A watches, listens, checks, and praises.

6. Repeat for remaining problems starting at step 2.

Cooperative Learning and Pre-Algebra: Becky Bride
Kagan Publishing • 1 (800) 933-2667 • www.KaganOnline.com

ACTIVITY

2 ADJUST MY NEGATIVE SIGN

Algebraic

1. Teacher poses many problems using Transparency 4.2.1.

2. Partner A rewrites problem one two different ways so it is equivalent, but the negative sign is in a different place each time, recording his/her responses on the paper.

3. Partner B watches, listens, checks, and praises.

4. Partner B rewrites the coefficient in the next problem two different ways so it is equivalent, with the negative sign in a different place each time, recording his/her responses on the paper.

5. Partner A watches, listens, checks, and praises.

6. Repeat for remaining problems starting at step 2.

▶ **Structure**
• RallyCoach

▶ **Materials**
• Transparency 4.2.1
• 1 sheet of paper and pencil per pair of students

ACTIVITY

3 GRAPH MY INEQUALITY

Graphic

Setup:
In pairs, Student A is the Sage; Student B is the Scribe. Students fold a sheet of paper in half and each writes his/her name on one half.

1. The Sage gives the Scribe step-by-step instructions on how to graph problem one on a number line.

2. The Scribe records the Sage's solution step-by-step in writing on the Sage's side of the paper.

3. If the Sage is correct, the Scribe praises the Sage. Otherwise, the Scribe coaches, then praises.

4. Students switch roles for the next problem.

▶ **Structure**
• Sage-N-Scribe

▶ **Materials**
• Transparency 4.2.2
• 1 sheet of paper and pencil per pair of students

Cooperative Learning and Pre-Algebra: Becky Bride
Kagan Publishing • 1 (800) 933-2667 • www.KaganOnline.com

ACTIVITY

4

WHERE DO YOU BELONG?

▶ **Structure**
 • Corners

▶ **Materials**
 • Fraction Cards (Blackline 4.1.6)
 • Transparency 4.2.3
 • 1 sheet of paper and pencil per student

Algebraic

1. Teacher gives each student a fraction card.

2. Students mix around the room trading cards.

3. Teacher announces different inequalities for each corner of the room using Transparency 4.2.3.

4. Students look at the number on their fraction card, comparing it to each inequality in each corner of the room.

5. Each student moves to the corner to which his/her number belongs.

6. Pairs are formed within each corner.

7. Using RallyTable, pairs share the sum, product, difference, or quotient of the numbers on their card, writing his/her responses on his/her paper.

8. Students trade cards with someone in their corner.

9. Repeat steps 2–8 with the next set of inequalities on the transparency.

Note: During the corner phase, students could line up in numerical order; get in groups of three and find the sum, product, or difference of the numbers; or state to which set(s) the number(s) belong. This is an excellent opportunity for reviewing concepts.

ACTIVITY

5

EVALUATE MY EXPRESSION

▶ **Structure**
 • Sage-N-Scribe

▶ **Materials**
 • Transparency 4.2.4
 • 1 sheet of paper and pencil per pair of students

Algebraic

Setup:
In pairs, Student A is the Sage; Student B is the Scribe. Students fold a sheet of paper in half and each writes his/her name on one half.

1. The Sage gives the Scribe step-by-step instructions on how to evaluate problem one.

2. The Scribe records the Sage's solution step-by-step in writing on the Sage's side of the paper.

3. If the Sage is correct, the Scribe praises the Sage. Otherwise, the Scribe coaches, then praises.

4. Students switch roles for the next problem.

Cooperative Learning and Pre-Algebra: Becky Bride
Kagan Publishing • 1 (800) 933-2667 • www.KaganOnline.com

ACTIVITY

6

EVALUATE ME SIMULTANEOUSLY

Algebraic

Setup:
Teammate 1 writes problem one at the top of his/her paper and the values of each variable. Teammate 2 writes problem two at the top of his/her paper and the values of each variable. Teammate 3 writes problem three at the top of his/her paper and the values of each variable. Teammate 4 writes problem four at the top of his/her paper and the values of each variable.

Round One
1. All four students respond simultaneously by substituting the numbers for the appropriate variables found at the top of their paper into the expression and initialing his/her work.

2. Students signal they are done by turning over their paper so they can work at their own pace.

3. Students pass papers one person clockwise. Each teammate checks to see if the numbers were substituted correctly on the paper he/she received, coaching the teammate who did the work if it is incorrect. Then all four students respond simultaneously by performing the first operation which should be done based on the order of operations the students learned in lesson 1, and initialing his/her work.

4. Students signal they are done by turning over their paper so they can work at their own pace.

5. Students pass their papers one person clockwise. Each teammate checks the work on the paper he/she received coaching the teammate who did the work if it is incorrect. Then all four students respond simultaneously by performing the next operation and initialing his/her work.

6. Students signal they are done by turning over their paper so they can work at their own pace.

7. Students pass their papers one person clockwise. Each teammate checks the work on the paper he/she received coaching the teammate who did the problem if it is incorrect. Then all four students respond simultaneously by performing the final operation and initialing his/her work.

8. Students signal they are done by turning over their paper so they can work at their own pace.

9. Students pass their papers one person clockwise. Each teammate checks the work on the paper he/she received, coaching the teammate who did the work if it is incorrect.

▶ **Structure**
· Simultaneous RoundTable

▶ **Materials**
· Transparency 4.2.5
· 1 sheet of paper and pencil per student

ACTIVITY
7   SIMPLIFY MY EXPRESSION

▶ **Structure**
· Sage-N-Scribe

▶ **Materials**
· Transparency 4.2.6
· 1 sheet of paper and pencil per pair of students

Algebraic

Setup:
In pairs, Student A is the Sage; Student B is the Scribe. Students fold a sheet of paper in half and each writes his/her name on one half.

1. The Sage gives the Scribe step-by-step instructions on how to simplify problem one.

Answers:

1. $\frac{20}{3}x - \frac{1}{4}y$

2. $\frac{-11}{9}m + \frac{19}{12}$

3. $\frac{27}{10}w + \frac{11}{42}wh$

4. $\frac{73}{63}d + 2$

5. $\frac{7}{3}g - \frac{13}{8}n$

6. $\frac{67}{9}dc - \frac{31}{15}d$

7. $\frac{7}{48}h - \frac{9}{8}$

8. $-\frac{71}{16} + \frac{16}{21}u$

2. The Scribe records the Sage's solution step-by-step in writing on the Sage's side of the paper.

3. If the Sage is correct, the Scribe praises the Sage. Otherwise, the Scribe coaches, then praises.

4. Students switch roles for the next problem.

ACTIVITY
8   WRITE ME USING SYMBOLS

▶ **Structure**
· Sage-N-Scribe

▶ **Materials**
· Blackline 4.2.7
· 1 sheet of paper and pencil per pair of students

Algebraic

Setup:
In pairs, Student A is the Sage; Student B is the Scribe. Students fold a sheet of paper in half and each writes his/her name on one half.

1. The Sage gives the Scribe step-by-step instructions on how to write problem one using symbols.

2. The Scribe records the Sage's solution step-by-step in writing on the Sage's side of the paper.

3. If the Sage is correct, the Scribe praises the Sage. Otherwise, the Scribe coaches, then praises.

4. Students switch roles for the next problem.

Cooperative Learning and Pre-Algebra: Becky Bride
Kagan Publishing • 1 (800) 933-2667 • www.KaganOnline.com

ACTIVITY

9 WHAT DID WE LEARN?

Synthesis

1. Each teammate signs his/ her name in the upper right corner of the team paper with the colored pen/pencil he/she is using.

2. One teammate writes *"Fractions in Expressions"* in the center of the team paper in a rectangle.

3. Teammate 1 shares with the team one core concept he/she learned in the unit.

4. The student checks for consensus.

5. The teammates show agreement or lack of agreement with thumbs up or down.

6. If there is agreement, the students celebrate and the teammate records the core concept on the graphic organizer, connecting it with a line to the main idea, Integers. If not, teammates discuss the response until there is agreement and then they celebrate.

7. Play continues with the next student's core concept, until all core concepts are exhausted.

8. Repeat steps 3–7 with teammates adding details to each core concept and making bridges between related ideas.

▶ **Structure**
· RoundTable Consensus

▶ **Materials**
· 1 large sheet of paper per team
· 1 different colored pen or pencil for each student in the team

REWRITE MY COEFFICIENT ADJUST MY NEGATIVE SIGN

Structure: RallyCoach

Directions:

Activity 1: Rewrite each as an equivalent expression with a fractional coefficient.

Activity 2: Rewrite each problem two different ways so both are equivalent, but the negative sign is in a different place each time.

1. $\dfrac{3m}{-5}$ 2. $\dfrac{-k}{11}$ 3. $\dfrac{-u}{7}$ 4. $-\dfrac{7a}{6}$

5. $-\dfrac{6h}{11}$ 6. $\dfrac{12v}{-7}$ 7. $\dfrac{-3w}{8}$ 8. $\dfrac{d}{-5}$

Answers for Activity 1:

1. $\dfrac{3}{-5}m$ 2. $\dfrac{-1}{11}k$ 3. $\dfrac{-1}{7}u$ 4. $-\dfrac{7}{6}a$

5. $-\dfrac{6}{11}h$ 6. $\dfrac{12}{-7}v$ 7. $\dfrac{-3}{8}w$ 8. $\dfrac{1}{-5}d$

Answers for Activity 2:

1. $\dfrac{-3}{5}m$ or $-\dfrac{3}{5}m$ 2. $\dfrac{1}{-11}k$ or $-\dfrac{1}{11}k$ 3. $\dfrac{1}{-7}u$ or $-\dfrac{1}{7}u$ 4. $\dfrac{-7}{6}a$ or $\dfrac{7}{-6}a$

5. $\dfrac{-6}{11}h$ or $\dfrac{6}{-11}h$ 6. $\dfrac{-12}{7}v$ or $-\dfrac{12}{7}v$ 7. $\dfrac{3}{-8}w$ or $-\dfrac{3}{8}w$ 8. $\dfrac{-1}{5}d$ or $-\dfrac{1}{5}d$

Cooperative Learning and Pre-Algebra: Becky Bride
Kagan Publishing • 1 (800) 933-2667 • www.KaganOnline.com

GRAPH MY INEQUALITY

Structure: Sage-N-Scribe

Graph each inequality on a number line.

1. $x > 4\dfrac{3}{5}$

2. $-1\dfrac{2}{3} \geq m$

3. $1\dfrac{1}{6} \leq x$

4. $w < 2\dfrac{3}{7}$

5. $h > -2\dfrac{5}{8}$

6. $1\dfrac{5}{9} < k$

7. $-1\dfrac{2}{3} \leq y < \dfrac{3}{4}$

8. $\dfrac{-5}{6} \geq u > -3\dfrac{5}{12}$

Answers will vary.

ACTIVITY 4 WHERE DO YOU BELONG?

Structure: Corners

Listen to the teacher for instructions.

Round 1:

1. $x \geq \dfrac{10}{3}$

2. $\dfrac{3}{8} \leq x < \dfrac{10}{3}$

3. $\dfrac{-15}{8} \leq x < \dfrac{3}{8}$

4. $\dfrac{-15}{8} > x$

Round 2:

1. $h < -\dfrac{17}{4}$

2. $-\dfrac{17}{4} \leq h \leq \dfrac{1}{-6}$

3. $\dfrac{-1}{6} < h < \dfrac{5}{4}$

4. $\dfrac{5}{4} \leq h$

Cooperative Learning and Pre-Algebra: Becky Bride
Kagan Publishing • 1 (800) 933-2667 • www.KaganOnline.com

EVALUATE MY EXPRESSION

Structure: Sage-N-Scribe

Evaluate each of the following if

$$m = \frac{-1}{2} \qquad w = 1\frac{1}{4} \qquad p = \frac{4}{-3} \qquad h = \frac{7}{12}$$

1. $2m - 3p$

2. $w^2 - 4m$

3. $ph - w$

4. $h - 2wp$

5. $w(w + p)$

6. $h - mp$

7. $\dfrac{m}{h} - p^2$

8. $3w + \dfrac{p}{h}$

Answers:

1. 3 　　 2. $\frac{57}{16} = 3\frac{9}{16}$ 　　 3. $-\frac{73}{36} = \left(-2\frac{1}{36}\right)$ 　　 4. $\frac{47}{12} = 3\frac{11}{12}$

5. $-\frac{5}{48}$ 　　 6. $-\frac{1}{12}$ 　　 7. $-\frac{166}{63} = \left(-2\frac{40}{63}\right)$ 　　 8. $\frac{41}{28} = 1\frac{13}{28}$

ACTIVITY
6

EVALUATE ME SIMULTANEOUSLY

Structure: Simultaneous RoundTable

Evaluate using: $n = \dfrac{-3}{2}$, $w = \dfrac{5}{6}$, and $d = \dfrac{7}{-4}$

1. $w - n^2 + 2d$

2. $\dfrac{nd}{w} + n$

3. $w(n^2 - 2d)$

4. $2d - \dfrac{n^2}{w}$

Answers:

1. $-\dfrac{59}{12} = \left(-4\dfrac{11}{12}\right)$ 2. $\dfrac{33}{20} = 1\dfrac{13}{20}$ 3. $\dfrac{115}{24} = 4\dfrac{19}{24}$ 4. $-\dfrac{31}{5} = \left(-6\dfrac{1}{5}\right)$

Cooperative Learning and Pre-Algebra: Becky Bride
Kagan Publishing • 1 (800) 933-2667 • www.KaganOnline.com

SIMPLIFY MY EXPRESSION

Structure: Sage-N-Scribe

Simplify each expression.

1. $\dfrac{2}{3}x - \dfrac{3}{4}y + 6x + \dfrac{1}{2}y$

2. $\dfrac{-5}{9}m - \dfrac{2}{3} + \left(\dfrac{3}{2}\right)^2 - \dfrac{2}{3}m$

3. $\dfrac{7}{2}w - \dfrac{1}{6}wh - \dfrac{4}{5}w + \dfrac{3}{7}wh$

4. $\left(\dfrac{-1}{3}\right)^2 d + \dfrac{12}{7}d - \dfrac{2}{3}d + 2$

5. $4g - \dfrac{3}{8}n - \dfrac{5}{4}n - \dfrac{5}{3}g$

6. $8dc - \dfrac{5}{3}d - \dfrac{5}{9}dc - \dfrac{2}{5}d$

7. $\left(\dfrac{1}{4}\right)^2 h - \dfrac{7}{6}h - \dfrac{9}{8} + \dfrac{5}{4}h$

8. $-5 - \dfrac{4}{7}u + \left(\dfrac{3}{4}\right)^2 + \dfrac{4}{3}u$

Answers in teacher's notes.

ACTIVITY

8 WRITE ME USING SYMBOLS

Structure: Sage-N-Scribe

Rewrite each using symbols.

1. Three-fourths of some number increased by three

2. Half of some number decreased by five-sevenths

3. Two-thirds times the sum of some number and five-ninths

4. Seven-fourths subtracted from the quotient of some number and one-half

5. Six divided by the product of three-tenths and some number

6. Five-sixths of some number increased by seven-eighths of a different number

7. The area of a rectangle if the width is two-thirds of the length

8. The area of a triangle whose base is nine-fifths of the height

Answers:

1. $\frac{3}{4}m + 3$ 2. $\frac{1}{2}y - \frac{5}{7}$ 3. $\frac{2}{3}\left(x + \frac{5}{9}\right)$ 4. $\left(m \div \frac{1}{2}\right) - \frac{7}{4}$

5. $6 \div \left(\frac{3}{10}m\right)$ 6. $\frac{5}{6}x + \frac{7}{8}y$ 7. $\frac{2}{3} \times L \times L = \frac{2}{3}L^2$ 8. $\frac{9}{10} \times h \times h = \frac{9}{10}h^2$

Cooperative Learning and Pre-Algebra: Becky Bride
Kagan Publishing • 1 (800) 933-2667 • www.KaganOnline.com

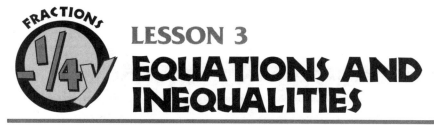

LESSON 3
EQUATIONS AND INEQUALITIES

This lesson reinforces solving one- and two-step equations and inequalities. The problems in this lesson have fractional coefficients, constants, and answers. The students will be required to graph their inequality answers, reinforcing graphing on a number line. The lesson ends with geometric applications and a synthesis activity.

SOLVE MY ONE-STEP EQUATION

Algebraic

Setup:
In pairs, Student A is the Sage; Student B is the Scribe. Students fold a sheet of paper in half and each writes his/her name on one half.

1. The Sage gives the Scribe step-by-step instructions on how to solve problem one.

2. The Scribe records the Sage's solution step-by-step in writing on the Sage's side of the paper.

3. If the Sage is correct, the Scribe praises the Sage. Otherwise, the Scribe coaches, then praises.

4. Students switch roles for the next problem.

▶ **Structure**
•Sage-N-Scribe

▶ **Materials**
•Transparency 4.3.1
• 1 sheet of paper and pencil per pair of students

SOLVE MY TWO-STEP EQUATION

Algebraic

Setup:
In pairs, Student A is the Sage; Student B is the Scribe. Students fold a sheet of paper in half and each writes his/her name on one half.

1. The Sage gives the Scribe step-by-step instructions on how to solve problem one.

2. The Scribe records the Sage's solution step-by-step in writing on the Sage's side of the paper.

3. If the Sage is correct, the Scribe praises the Sage. Otherwise, the Scribe coaches, then praises.

4. Students switch roles for the next problem.

▶ **Structure**
•Sage-N-Scribe

▶ **Materials**
•Transparency 4.3.2
• 1 sheet of paper and pencil per pair of students

Cooperative Learning and Pre-Algebra: Becky Bride
Kagan Publishing • 1 (800) 933-2667 • www.KaganOnline.com

3 SOLVE MY ONE-STEP INEQUALITY

▶ **Structure**
• Sage-N-Scribe

▶ **Materials**
• Transparency 4.3.3
• 1 sheet of paper and pencil per pair of students

Algebraic/Graphic

Setup:
In pairs, Student A is the Sage; Student B is the Scribe. Students fold a sheet of paper in half and each writes his/her name on one half.

1. The Sage gives the Scribe step-by-step instructions on how to solve and graph problem one.

2. The Scribe records the Sage's solution step-by-step in writing on the Sage's side of the paper.

3. If the Sage is correct, the Scribe praises the Sage. Otherwise, the Scribe coaches, then praises.

4. Students switch roles for the next problem.

4 SOLVE MY TWO-STEP INEQUALITY

▶ **Structure**
• Sage-N-Scribe

▶ **Materials**
• Transparency 4.3.4
• 1 sheet of paper and pencil per pair of students

Algebraic/Graphic

Setup:
In pairs, Student A is the Sage; Student B is the Scribe. Students fold a sheet of paper in half and each writes his/her name on one half.

1. The Sage gives the Scribe step-by-step instructions on how to solve and graph problem one.

2. The Scribe records the Sage's solution step-by-step in writing on the Sage's side of the paper.

3. If the Sage is correct, the Scribe praises the Sage. Otherwise, the Scribe coaches, then praises.

4. Students switch roles for the next problem.

ACTIVITY 5

GEOMETRIC APPLICATIONS

Algebraic

Setup:
In pairs, Student A is the Sage; Student B is the Scribe. Students fold a sheet of paper in half and each writes his/her name on one half.

1. The Sage gives the Scribe step-by-step instructions on how to solve problem one.

2. The Scribe records the Sage's solution step-by-step in writing on the Sage's side of the paper.

3. If the Sage is correct, the Scribe praises the Sage. Otherwise, the Scribe coaches, then praises.

4. Students switch roles for the next problem.

▶ **Structure**
•Sage-N-Scribe

▶ **Materials**
•Blacklines 4.3.5 and 1.2.11 per pair of students
•1 sheet of paper and pencil per pair of students

ACTIVITY 6

WHAT DID WE LEARN?

Synthesis

1. Each teammate signs his/her name in the upper right corner of the team paper with the colored pen/pencil he/she is using.

2. One teammate writes "*Fractions*" in the center of the team paper in a rectangle.

3. Teammate 1 shares with the team one core concept he/she learned in the entire unit.

4. The student checks for consensus.

5. The teammates show agreement or lack of agreement with thumbs up or down.

6. If there is agreement, the students celebrate and the teammate records the core concept on the graphic organizer, connecting it with a line to the main idea, *Fractions, Equation and Inequalities*. If not, teammates discuss the response until there is agreement and then they celebrate.

7. Play continues with the next student's core concept, until all core concepts are exhausted.

8. Repeat steps 3–7 with teammates adding details to each core concept and making bridges between related ideas.

▶ **Structure**
•RoundTable Consensus

▶ **Materials**
• 1 large sheet of paper per team
• 1 different colored pen or pencil for each student in the team

ACTIVITY

1 SOLVE MY ONE-STEP EQUATION

Structure: Sage-N-Scribe

Solve each equation.

1. $-\dfrac{2}{3} + m = \dfrac{5}{9}$

2. $8 = \dfrac{-4}{5}h$

3. $\dfrac{-3}{5} = \dfrac{3}{4}y$

4. $w - \dfrac{3}{11} = \dfrac{3}{2}$

5. $m \div \left(-\dfrac{6}{7}\right) = \left(-\dfrac{2}{3}\right)$

6. $\dfrac{7}{4} + d = \dfrac{1}{3}$

7. $\dfrac{10}{9} = u - \dfrac{5}{-6}$

8. $-\dfrac{11}{3} = k \div \dfrac{5}{6}$

Answers:

1. $\dfrac{11}{9} = 1\dfrac{2}{9}$ 2. -10 3. $-\dfrac{4}{5}$ 4. $\dfrac{39}{22} = 1\dfrac{17}{22}$

5. $\dfrac{4}{7}$ 6. $\dfrac{-17}{12} = \left(-1\dfrac{5}{12}\right)$ 7. $\dfrac{5}{18}$ 8. $\dfrac{-55}{18} = \left(-3\dfrac{1}{18}\right)$

Cooperative Learning and Pre-Algebra: Becky Bride
Kagan Publishing • 1 (800) 933-2667 • www.KaganOnline.com

SOLVE MY TWO-STEP EQUATION

Structure: Sage-N-Scribe

Solve each equation.

1. $\dfrac{11}{3} = \dfrac{1}{6}x + 2$

2. $\dfrac{5}{9} = \dfrac{1}{3} - \dfrac{1}{6}u$

3. $-\dfrac{5}{4}y - \dfrac{2}{3} = \dfrac{5}{12}$

4. $\dfrac{5}{2} - 8m = \dfrac{1}{4}$

5. $-\dfrac{4}{5} = 3h - \dfrac{1}{4}$

6. $\dfrac{4}{7}k - 5 = \left(-\dfrac{2}{3}\right)$

7. $\dfrac{9}{4} - \dfrac{3}{2}n = \dfrac{5}{8}$

8. $-\dfrac{4}{3} = \dfrac{3}{5}y - 1$

9. $4 = \dfrac{1}{6}w - \dfrac{2}{3}$

10. $3p - \dfrac{2}{9} = (-2)$

Answers:

1. 10   2. $\dfrac{-4}{3}$ 3. $-\dfrac{13}{15}$ 4. $\dfrac{9}{32}$ 5. $-\dfrac{11}{60}$

6. $\dfrac{91}{12} = 7\dfrac{7}{12}$ 7. $\dfrac{13}{12} = 1\dfrac{1}{12}$ 8. $-\dfrac{5}{9}$ 9. 28   10. $-\dfrac{16}{27}$

ACTIVITY 3

SOLVE MY ONE-STEP INEQUALITY

Structure: Sage-N-Scribe

Solve each inequality and graph the answer on a number line.

1. $\dfrac{-3u}{7} \geq 6$

2. $g - \dfrac{5}{2} < \left(-\dfrac{1}{3}\right)$

3. $-\dfrac{1}{6} < \dfrac{4d}{5}$

4. $-\dfrac{2}{3}h > \left(-\dfrac{5}{4}\right)$

5. $\dfrac{4}{3} + x \leq 1$

6. $\dfrac{17}{8} + w < \dfrac{3}{4}$

7. $\dfrac{-1}{9} > \left(-\dfrac{2e}{5}\right)$

8. $\dfrac{4}{9} \geq \dfrac{5m}{3}$

9. $k - \dfrac{1}{8} \geq \left(\dfrac{-2}{3}\right)$

10. $6 < \left(-\dfrac{2n}{7}\right)$

Answers:

1. $u \leq (-14)$ 2. $g < \dfrac{13}{6}$ 3. $-\dfrac{5}{24} < d$ 4. $h < \dfrac{15}{8}$ 5. $x \leq \left(-\dfrac{1}{3}\right)$

6. $w < \left(-\dfrac{11}{8}\right)$ 7. $\dfrac{5}{18} < e$ 8. $\dfrac{4}{15} \geq m$ 9. $k \geq \left(-\dfrac{13}{24}\right)$ 10. $-21 > n$

Cooperative Learning and Pre-Algebra: Becky Bride
Kagan Publishing • 1 (800) 933-2667 • www.KaganOnline.com

ACTIVITY 4

SOLVE MY TWO-STEP INEQUALITY

Structure: Sage-N-Scribe

Solve each inequality and graph the answer on a number line.

1. $\dfrac{-3m}{5} + 6 > \dfrac{1}{2}$

2. $-\dfrac{5}{7} > \dfrac{1}{4} - \dfrac{v}{2}$

3. $\dfrac{1}{3} + \dfrac{2h}{5} \leq \dfrac{13}{15}$

4. $\dfrac{5}{9} - \dfrac{4k}{3} < \dfrac{11}{18}$

5. $\dfrac{5}{8} > \dfrac{1}{2} - 4p$

6. $-\dfrac{17}{6} < \dfrac{2n}{3} - 2$

7. $-1\dfrac{1}{6} \geq \dfrac{2}{3} - \dfrac{u}{5}$

8. $\dfrac{3e}{4} + \dfrac{5}{8} > \dfrac{7}{16}$

9. $9 - \dfrac{a}{6} < 8\dfrac{1}{2}$

10. $-3x + \dfrac{5}{8} \geq 3\dfrac{1}{2}$

Answers:

1. $m < \dfrac{55}{6}$ 2. $\dfrac{27}{14} < v$ 3. $h \leq \dfrac{4}{3}$ 4. $k > \left(-\dfrac{1}{24}\right)$ 5. $-\dfrac{1}{32} < p$

6. $-\dfrac{5}{4} < n$ 7. $\dfrac{55}{6} \leq u$ 8. $e > \left(-\dfrac{1}{4}\right)$ 9. $a > 3$ 10. $x \leq \left(-\dfrac{23}{24}\right)$

ACTIVITY
5 **GEOMETRIC APPLICATIONS**

Structure: Sage-N-Scribe

Solve each problem below. Use $\pi = \frac{22}{7}$.

1. If the width of a rectangle is $2\frac{3}{4}$ centimeters and the area is 12 square centimeters, find the length.

2. What is the radius of a circle if the circumference is 33 centimeters?

3. The volume of a cylindrical can is $18\frac{3}{4}$ cubic centimeters. If the radius is $\frac{3}{2}$ centimeters, find the height of the can.

4. The perimeter of a square table is $16\frac{1}{2}$ feet. What is the length of each side?

5. Fritz is making a box whose height is $4\frac{1}{2}$ inches and width is 5 inches. How long must the box be so its volume is $120\frac{3}{4}$ cubic inches?

Cooperative Learning and Pre-Algebra: Becky Bride
Kagan Publishing • 1 (800) 933-2667 • www.KaganOnline.com

5 GEOMETRIC APPLICATIONS

Structure: Sage-N-Scribe

6. Find the surface area of a spherical piñata if its radius is $5\frac{1}{2}$ inches.

7. William wants to carpet his bedroom. The room is rectangular and its dimensions are $12\frac{3}{4}$ feet by $11\frac{2}{3}$ feet. How many square feet of carpet does he need (write as a mixed number)? If carpeting costs $3.99 per square foot, how much will it cost to carpet his room? (Round answer to the nearest cent.)

8. Kristin wants to paint the walls of her rectangular living room. The dimensions of the room are $15\frac{2}{3}$ feet by 18 feet. The walls are eight feet tall. What is the total area to be painted (write as a mixed number)? She will need to use two coats of paint. If each gallon of paint covers 300 square feet, how many gallons does she need? Round to the nearest gallon.

Answers:

1. $4\frac{4}{11}$ cm   2. $5\frac{1}{4}$ cm   3. $2\frac{43}{66}$ cm   4. $4\frac{1}{8}$ ft

5. $5\frac{11}{30}$ in.   6. $380\frac{2}{7}$ in.²   7. $148\frac{3}{4}$ ft², $593.51   8. $538\frac{2}{3}$ ft², 4 gal

RATIO, PROPORTION, AND PERCENT

This chapter has two lessons—the first one has students work with ratio and proportion and the second one has students work with percents. Since ratio and proportions are first, students can use proportions to solve percent problems. Both lessons contain applications.

LESSON
1 **RATIO AND PROPORTION**

ACTIVITY 1: Write My Ratio
ACTIVITY 2: Am I a Ratio or Rate?
ACTIVITY 3: What Is My Rate?
ACTIVITY 4: Am I a Proportion?
ACTIVITY 5: Solve My Proportion
ACTIVITY 6: Set Me Up Two Ways
ACTIVITY 7: Apply Me
ACTIVITY 8: What Did We Learn?

LESSON
2 **PERCENTS**

ACTIVITY 1: Rewrite My Fraction as a Percent
ACTIVITY 2: Rewrite My Decimal as a Percent
ACTIVITY 3: Rewrite My Percent
ACTIVITY 4: Applications
ACTIVITY 5: Financial Applications
ACTIVITY 6: Percent Increase/Decrease
ACTIVITY 7: Geometric Applications
ACTIVITY 8: All Mixed Up
ACTIVITY 9: What Did We Learn?

LESSON 1
RATIO AND PROPORTION

This lesson works with ratios, rates, and proportions. It begins with students writing ratios, given data in a table. The next lesson has students distinguish between rates and ratios. In Activity 3 students are given a word sentence and asked to write the appropriate rate. Activity 4 connects ratios to proportions. Then students solve proportions algebraically. Activity 6 has students set up word problems in two different ways. Students will use proportions to solve real-world problems in Activity 7. This lesson ends with an activity where students will synthesize their learning.

ACTIVITY 1
WRITE MY RATIO

▶ **Structure**
• RallyCoach

▶ **Materials**
• Blackline 5.1.1 per pair of students
• 1 sheet of paper and pencil per pair of students

Numeric

1. Teacher poses many problems using Transparency 5.1.1.

2. Partner A writes a ratio for problem one on the paper.

3. Partner B watches, listens, checks, and praises.

4. Partner B writes a ratio for the next problem on the paper.

5. Partner A watches, listens, checks, and praises.

6. Repeat for remaining problems starting at step 2.

ACTIVITY 2
AM I A RATIO OR RATE?

▶ **Structure**
• RallyRobin

▶ **Materials**
• Transparency 5.1.2

Numeric

1. Teacher poses multiple problems using Transparency 5.1.2.

2. In pairs, students take turns orally stating whether the expression in the problem is a rate or ratio, justifying their answer.

Cooperative Learning and Pre-Algebra: Becky Bride
Kagan Publishing • 1 (800) 933-2667 • www.KaganOnline.com

ACTIVITY 3
WHAT IS MY RATE?

Numeric

1. Teacher poses many problems using Transparency 5.1.3.

2. Partner A writes the rate as a decimal for problem one on the paper.

3. Partner B watches, listens, checks, and praises.

4. Partner B writes the rate as a decimal for the next problem on the paper.

5. Partner A watches, listens, checks, and praises.

6. Repeat for remaining problems starting at step 2.

▶ **Structure**
• RallyCoach

▶ **Materials**
• Transparency 5.1.3
• 1 sheet of paper and pencil per pair of students

ACTIVITY 4
AM I A PROPORTION?

Numeric

1. Teacher poses many problems using Transparency 5.1.4.

2. Partner A determines whether the two ratios in problem one can form a proportion and writes his/her response on the paper explaining his/her reasoning.

3. Partner B watches, listens, checks, and praises.

4. Partner B determines whether the two ratios in the next problem can form a proportion and writes his/her response on the paper explaining his/her reasoning.

5. Partner A watches, listens, checks, and praises.

6. Repeat for remaining problems starting at step 2.

▶ **Structure**
• RallyCoach

▶ **Materials**
• Transparency 5.1.4
• 1 sheet of paper and pencil per pair of students

ACTIVITY

5

SOLVE MY PROPORTION

▶ **Structure:**
• Sage-N-Scribe

▶ **Materials**
• Transparency 5.1.5
• 1 sheet of paper and pencil per pair of students

Algebraic

Setup:
In pairs, Student A is the Sage; Student B is the Scribe. Students fold a sheet of paper in half and each writes his/her name on one half.

1. The Sage gives the Scribe step-by-step instructions on how to solve problem one.

2. The Scribe records the Sage's solution step-by-step in writing on the Sage's side of the paper.

3. If the Sage is correct, the Scribe praises the Sage. Otherwise, the Scribe coaches, then praises.

4. Students switch roles for the next problem.

ACTIVITY

6

SET ME UP TWO WAYS

▶ **Structure**
• RallyCoach

▶ **Materials**
• Blackline 5.1.6 per pair of students
• 1 sheet of paper and pencil per pair of students

Algebraic

1. Teacher poses many problems using Blackline 5.1.6.

2. Partner A writes two different proportions for problem one on the paper.

3. Partner B watches, listens, checks, and praises.

4. Partner B writes two different proportions for the next problem on the paper.

5. Partner A watches, listens, checks, and praises.

6. Repeat for remaining problems starting at step 2.

Answers:

1. $\frac{15}{x} = \frac{6}{29}$ or $\frac{x}{15} = \frac{29}{6}$

2. $\frac{1,200}{1.5} = \frac{70,000}{x}$ or $\frac{1.5}{1,200} = \frac{x}{70,000}$

3. $\frac{16}{14} = \frac{x}{20}$ or $\frac{14}{16} = \frac{20}{x}$

4. $\frac{6,200}{0.75} = \frac{12,000}{x}$ or $\frac{0.75}{6,200} = \frac{x}{12,000}$

5. $\frac{3}{3.29} = \frac{x}{10}$ or $\frac{3.29}{3} = \frac{10}{x}$

6. $\frac{1/2}{30} = \frac{x}{140}$ or $\frac{30}{1/2} = \frac{140}{x}$

7. $\frac{1/8}{1} = \frac{21/16}{x}$ or $\frac{1}{1/8} = \frac{x}{21/16}$

8. $\frac{1.5}{12} = \frac{x}{30}$ or $\frac{12}{1.5} = \frac{30}{x}$

9. $\frac{8,000}{x} = \frac{2.5}{1}$ or $\frac{x}{8,000} = \frac{1}{2.5}$

10. $\frac{2}{3.5} = \frac{x}{20}$ or $\frac{3.5}{2} = \frac{20}{x}$

7 APPLY ME

Algebraic

Setup:
In pairs, Student A is the Sage; Student B is the Scribe. Students fold a sheet of paper in half and each writes his/her name on one half.

1. The Sage gives the Scribe step-by-step instructions on how to solve problem one.

2. The Scribe records the Sage's solution step-by-step in writing on the Sage's side of the paper.

3. If the Sage is correct, the Scribe praises the Sage. Otherwise, the Scribe coaches, then praises.

4. Students switch roles for the next problem.

Answers:

1. 73 deer	2. 87.5 gal
3. 23 lbs	4. 1.45 hr
5. 9.1 lbs	6. 2.33 in.
7. 10.5 ft	8. 3.75 lbs
9. 53.33 hr	10. 11 lbs

▶ **Structure**
• Sage-N-Scribe

▶ **Materials**
• Blackline 5.1.6 per pair of students
• 1 sheet of paper and pencil per pair of students

8 WHAT DID WE LEARN?

Synthesis

1. Each teammate signs his/her name in the upper right corner of the team paper with the colored pen/pencil he/she is using.

2. One teammate writes "*Ratio and Proportions*" in the center of the team paper in a rectangle.

3. Teammate 1 shares with the team one core concept he/she learned in the entire unit.

4. The student checks for consensus.

5. The teammates show agreement or lack of agreement with thumbs up or down.

6. If there is agreement, the students celebrate and the teammate records the core concept on the graphic organizer, connecting it with a line to the main idea, *Ratio and Proportions*. If not, teammates discuss the response until there is agreement and then they celebrate.

7. Play continues with the next student's core concept, until all core concepts are exhausted.

8. Repeat steps 3–7 with teammates adding details to each core concept and making bridges between related ideas.

▶ **Structure**
• RoundTable Consensus

▶ **Materials**
• 1 large sheet of paper per team
• 1 different colored pen or pencil for each student in the team

Chapter 5: Ratio, Proportion, and Percent

Lesson One

WRITE MY RATIO

Structure: RallyCoach

For problems 1–6, use the table below and write the requested ratio, as a fraction, in simplified form.

Pets at the Humane Society

Type	Dogs	Cats	Rabbits	Birds	Snakes
Number	24	32	8	10	6

1. dogs to cats

2. snakes to birds

3. rabbits to total animals

4. cats to snakes

5. birds to rabbits

6. dogs to total animals

For problems 7–12, use the table below and write the requested ratio, as a fraction, in simplified form.

Survey of People on a Beach

	Females	Males
Surfers	12	10
Non-surfers	15	14

7. female surfers to male surfers surveyed

8. male non-surfers to total males surveyed

9. female non-surfers to male surfers surveyed

10. male non-surfers to total number of people surveyed

11. female non-surfers to total number of people surveyed

12. female surfers to total females surveyed

Answers:

1. $\frac{3}{4}$ 2. $\frac{3}{5}$ 3. $\frac{1}{10}$ 4. $\frac{16}{3}$ 5. $\frac{5}{4}$ 6. $\frac{3}{10}$

7. $\frac{6}{5}$ 8. $\frac{7}{12}$ 9. $\frac{3}{2}$ 10. $\frac{14}{51}$ 11. $\frac{5}{17}$ 12. $\frac{4}{9}$

Cooperative Learning and Pre-Algebra: Becky Bride
Kagan Publishing • 1 (800) 933-2667 • www.KaganOnline.com

2 AM I A RATIO OR RATE?

Structure: RallyRobin

State whether each of the following is a rate or ratio and justify your answer.

1. $\dfrac{9 \text{ feet}}{5 \text{ inches}}$

2. $\dfrac{9 \text{ feet}}{7 \text{ seconds}}$

3. $\dfrac{16 \text{ dollars}}{5 \text{ ounces}}$

4. $\dfrac{6 \text{ dogs in a shelter}}{19 \text{ animals in a shelter}}$

5. $\dfrac{100 \text{ miles}}{3 \text{ gallons}}$

6. $\dfrac{7 \text{ ounces}}{2 \text{ pounds}}$

Answers:
1. ratio   2. rate   3. rate   4. ratio   5. rate   6. ratio

Cooperative Learning and Pre-Algebra: Becky Bride
Kagan Publishing • 1 (800) 933-2667 • www.KaganOnline.com

ACTIVITY

3 WHAT IS MY RATE?

Structure: RallyCoach

Write each rate below as a decimal rounded to the hundredths place.

1. Amy drove three hundred twenty-four miles on nine gallons of gas.

2. Cody bought two pounds of pecans for $15.50.

3. In five seconds, the rocket traveled seventy feet.

4. Twenty-five ounces of peanut butter costs $6.59.

5. In four hours, fifty-two fish were caught.

6. The caterpillar ate seven-tenths pounds of leaves in three days.

Answers:

1. 36 mi/gal	2. 7.75 $/lbs	3. 14 ft/sec
4. 0.26 $/oz	5. 13 fish/hr	6. 0.23 lb/day

Cooperative Learning and Pre-Algebra: Becky Bride
Kagan Publishing • 1 (800) 933-2667 • www.KaganOnline.com

4 AM I A PROPORTION?

Structure: RallyCoach

Determine whether the two ratios in each problem can form a proportion. Explain your reasoning.

1. $\dfrac{24}{9}$ and $\dfrac{16}{6}$

2. $\dfrac{4}{9}$ and $\dfrac{5}{11}$

3. $\dfrac{12}{15}$ and $\dfrac{5}{6}$

4. $\dfrac{20}{12}$ and $\dfrac{15}{9}$

5. $\dfrac{0.5}{3}$ and $\dfrac{1.5}{9}$

6. $\dfrac{2/3}{8}$ and $\dfrac{3/2}{18}$

7. $\dfrac{12}{0.3}$ and $\dfrac{0.4}{0.1}$

8. $\dfrac{2.4}{0.06}$ and $\dfrac{30}{0.75}$

Answers:

1. yes	2. no	3. no	4. yes
5. yes	6. yes	7. no	8. yes

ACTIVITY 5
SOLVE MY PROPORTION

Structure: Sage-N-Scribe

Solve each proportion. For problems 1–6, round answers to the nearest thousandth. For problems 7–8, fractional answers need to be in simplest form.

1. $\dfrac{5}{m} = \dfrac{8}{3}$

2. $\dfrac{9}{5} = \dfrac{h}{0.3}$

3. $\dfrac{w}{1.4} = \dfrac{9}{11}$

4. $\dfrac{5}{2} = \dfrac{6}{u}$

5. $\dfrac{2}{3c} = \dfrac{9}{5}$

6. $\dfrac{4x}{15} = \dfrac{3}{10}$

7. $\dfrac{1/8}{2/9} = \dfrac{d}{3/4}$

8. $\dfrac{2/3}{n} = \dfrac{5/4}{3/7}$

Answers:

1. 1.875	2. 0.54	3. 1.145	4. 2.4
5. 0.370	6. 1.125	7. $\frac{27}{64}$	8. $\frac{8}{35}$

Cooperative Learning and Pre-Algebra: Becky Bride
Kagan Publishing • 1 (800) 933-2667 • www.KaganOnline.com

ACTIVITIES
6&7 SET ME UP TWO WAYS APPLY ME

Structure: RallyCoach (Activity 6)
Structure: Sage-N-Scribe (Activity 7)
Directions:
Activity 6: Write two different proportions for each problem.
Activity 7: Solve each proportion written in Activity 6.

1. To estimate a deer population, forest rangers tagged fifteen deer. Six months later, they captured twenty-nine deer and of those captured, six were tagged. Estimate the number of deer in the forest. Round your answer to the nearest whole number.

2. Mosquito Control has a pesticide that covers one thousand two hundred square feet for each one and a half gallons used. How many gallons are needed to treat a seventy thousand square foot lake? Round your answer to the nearest tenth of a gallon.

3. The humane society uses sixteen pounds of dog food for fourteen dogs. If there are twenty dogs at the humane society, how much food is needed to feed them? Round your answer to the nearest pound.

4. Linda mows a six thousand, two hundred square foot lawn in three-fourths of an hour. How long will it take her to mow twelve thousand square feet? Round your answer to the nearest hundredth.

5. Three pounds of apples costs $3.29. How many pounds of apples can be purchased for $10? Round your answer to the nearest tenth.

SET ME UP TWO WAYS
APPLY ME

Structure: RallyCoach (Activity 6)
Structure: Sage-N-Scribe (Activity 7)

6. On a map the scale is half an inch is equal to thirty miles. How far apart are two cities on the map if they are actually one hundred forty miles apart? Round your answer to the nearest hundredth.

7. The scale on a blueprint is one foot is equal to one-eighth inch. How long is a wall that is one and five-sixteenths inches long on the blueprint? Round your answer to the nearest tenth.

8. Amy loves to hear the birds sing each morning, so she made a birdfeeder. If one and one half pounds of bird seed last twelve days, how many pounds of bird seed does she need for the month of September? Round your answer to the nearest hundredth.

9. A swimming pool holds eight thousand gallons of water. If water is flowing through a hose at a rate of two and one half gallons each minute, how long will it take to fill the pool? Put your answer in hours, then round to the nearest hundredth.

10. Brooke wants to make a nut mixture that contains two pounds of almonds for every three and one half pound of pecans. If she has twenty pounds of pecans, how many pounds of almonds does she need? Round your answer to the nearest pound.

Answers in teachers notes.

Cooperative Learning and Pre-Algebra: Becky Bride
Kagan Publishing • 1 (800) 933-2667 • www.KaganOnline.com

LESSON 2
PERCENTS

This lesson begins with students writing equivalent forms of fractions, decimals, and percents. The remainder of the lesson focuses on applications. First there are general applications, then financial applications, percent increase and decrease, geometric applications, and then an activity with all the applications mixed up. The lesson ends with a synthesis activity.

ACTIVITY

1 REWRITE MY FRACTION AS A PERCENT

Numeric

1. Teacher poses many problems using Transparency 5.2.1.

2. Partner A rewrites the fraction as a percent in problem one, recording his/her response on the paper.

3. Partner B watches, listens, checks, and praises.

4. Partner B rewrites the fraction in the next problem, recording his/her response on the paper.

5. Partner A watches, listens, checks, and praises.

6. Repeat for remaining problems starting at step 2.

▶ **Structure**
• RallyCoach

▶ **Materials**
• Transparency 5.2.1
• 1 sheet of paper and pencil per pair of students

ACTIVITY

2 REWRITE MY DECIMAL AS A PERCENT

Numeric

1. Teacher poses many problems using Transparency 5.2.2.

2. Partner A rewrites the decimal as a percent in problem one, recording his/her response on the paper.

3. Partner B watches, listens, checks, and praises.

4. Partner B rewrites the decimal in the next problem, recording his/her response on the paper.

5. Partner A watches, listens, checks, and praises.

6. Repeat for remaining problems starting at step 2.

▶ **Structure**
• RallyCoach

▶ **Materials**
• Transparency 5.2.2
• 1 sheet of paper and pencil per pair of students

ACTIVITY

3 REWRITE MY PERCENT

▶ **Structure**
· RallyCoach

▶ **Materials**
· Transparency 5.2.3
· 1 sheet of paper and pencil per pair of students

Numeric

1. Teacher poses many problems using Transparency 5.2.3.

2. Partner A rewrites the percent as a decimal in problem one, recording his/her response on the paper.

3. Partner B watches, listens, checks, and praises.

4. Partner B rewrites the percent in the next problem, recording his/her response on the paper.

5. Partner A watches, listens, checks, and praises.

6. Repeat for remaining problems starting at step 2.

7. Round 2: Repeat steps 2–6 rewriting the percent as a fraction.

ACTIVITY

4 APPLICATIONS

▶ **Structure**
· Sage-N-Scribe

▶ **Materials**
· Blackline 5.2.4 per pair of students
· 1 sheet of paper and pencil per pair of students

Numeric/Algebraic

Setup:
In pairs, Student A is the Sage; Student B is the Scribe. Students fold a sheet of paper in half and each writes his/her name on one half.

1. The Sage gives the Scribe step-by-step instructions on how to solve problem one.

2. The Scribe records the Sage's solution step-by-step in writing on the Sage's side of the paper.

3. If the Sage is correct, the Scribe praises the Sage. Otherwise, the Scribe coaches, then praises.

4. Students switch roles for the next problem.

Cooperative Learning and Pre-Algebra: Becky Bride
Kagan Publishing • 1 (800) 933-2667 • www.KaganOnline.com

ACTIVITY

5

FINANCIAL APPLICATIONS

Numeric/Algebraic

Setup:
In pairs, Student A is the Sage; Student B is the Scribe. Students fold a sheet of paper in half and each writes his/her name on one half.

1. The Sage gives the Scribe step-by-step instructions on how to solve problem one.

2. The Scribe records the Sage's solution step-by-step in writing on the Sage's side of the paper.

3. If the Sage is correct, the Scribe praises the Sage. Otherwise, the Scribe coaches, then praises.

4. Students switch roles for the next problem.

▶ **Structure**
•Sage-N-Scribe

▶ **Materials**
•Blackline 5.2.5 per pair of students
•1 sheet of paper and pencil per pair of students

ACTIVITY

6

PERCENT INCREASE/DECREASE

Numeric/Algebraic

Setup:
In pairs, Student A is the Sage; Student B is the Scribe. Students fold a sheet of paper in half and each writes his/her name on one half.

1. The Sage gives the Scribe step-by-step instructions on how to solve problem one.

2. The Scribe records the Sage's solution step-by-step in writing on the Sage's side of the paper.

3. If the Sage is correct, the Scribe praises the Sage. Otherwise, the Scribe coaches, then praises.

4. Students switch roles for the next problem.

▶ **Structure**
•Sage-N-Scribe

▶ **Materials**
•Blackline 5.2.6 per pair of students
•1 sheet of paper and pencil per pair of students

Chapter 5: Ratio, Proportion, and Percent

L e s s o n   T w o

7 GEOMETRIC APPLICATIONS

▶ **Structure**
· Sage-N-Scribe

▶ **Materials**
· Blackline 5.2.7 and 1.2.11 per pair of students
· 1 sheet of paper and pencil per pair of students

Numeric/Algebraic

Setup:
In pairs, Student A is the Sage; Student B is the Scribe. Students fold a sheet of paper in half and each writes his/her name on one half.

1. The Sage gives the Scribe step-by-step instructions on how to solve problem one.

2. The Scribe records the Sage's solution step-by-step in writing on the Sage's side of the paper.

3. If the Sage is correct, the Scribe praises the Sage. Otherwise, the Scribe coaches, then praises.

4. Students switch roles for the next problem.

8 ALL MIXED UP

▶ **Structure**
· Sage-N-Scribe

▶ **Materials**
· Blackline 5.2.8 and 1.2.11 per pair of students
· 1 sheet of paper and pencil per pair of students

Numeric/Algebraic

Setup:
In pairs, Student A is the Sage; Student B is the Scribe. Students fold a sheet of paper in half and each writes his/her name on one half.

1. The Sage gives the Scribe step-by-step instructions on how to solve problem one.

2. The Scribe records the Sage's solution step-by-step in writing on the Sage's side of the paper.

3. If the Sage is correct, the Scribe praises the Sage. Otherwise, the Scribe coaches, then praises.

4. Students switch roles for the next problem.

Cooperative Learning and Pre-Algebra: Becky Bride
Kagan Publishing · 1 (800) 933-2667 · www.KaganOnline.com

WHAT DID WE LEARN?

Synthesis

1. Each teammate signs his/her name in the upper right corner of the team paper with the colored pen/pencil he/she is using.

2. One teammate writes "*Percents*" in the center of the team paper in a rectangle.

3. Teammate 1 shares with the team one core concept he/she learned in the unit.

4. The student checks for consensus.

5. The teammates show agreement or lack of agreement with thumbs up or down.

6. If there is agreement, the students celebrate and the teammate records the core concept on the graphic organizer, connecting it with a line to the main idea, *Percents*. If not, teammates discuss the response until there is agreement and then they celebrate.

7. Play continues with the next student's core concept, until all core concepts are exhausted.

8. Repeat steps 3–7 with teammates adding details to each core concept and making bridges between related ideas.

▶ **Structure**
  · RoundTable Consensus

▶ **Materials**
  · 1 large sheet of paper per team
  · 1 different colored pen or pencil for each student in the team

Chapter 5: Ratio, Proportion, and Percent

Lesson Two

REWRITE MY FRACTION AS A PERCENT

Structure: RallyCoach

Rewrite each fraction as a percent. Round to the hundredths place when necessary.

1. $\dfrac{2}{3}$

2. $\dfrac{1}{12}$

3. $\dfrac{12}{5}$

4. $\dfrac{7}{9}$

5. $\dfrac{1}{15}$

6. $\dfrac{9}{5}$

7. $\dfrac{9}{4}$

8. $\dfrac{11}{8}$

9. $\dfrac{5}{6}$

10. $\dfrac{13}{4}$

Answers:

1. 67%	2. 8%	3. 240%	4. 78%	5. 7%
6. 180%	7. 225%	8. 138%	9. 83%	10. 325%

Cooperative Learning and Pre-Algebra: Becky Bride
Kagan Publishing • 1 (800) 933-2667 • www.KaganOnline.com

REWRITE MY DECIMAL AS A PERCENT

Structure: RallyCoach

Rewrite each number as a percent.

1. 0.32

2. 1.3

3. 6.7

4. 3

5. 0.153

6. 0.16

7. 4.09

8. 1.029

9. 7

10. 0.827

Answers:
1. 32%   2. 130%   3. 670%   4. 300%   5. 15.3%
6. 16%   7. 409%   8. 102.9%   9. 700%   10. 82.7%

REWRITE MY PERCENT

Structure: RallyCoach

Round 1: Rewrite each as a decimal
Round 2: Rewrite each as a fraction

1. 16%   2. 112%

3. 7%   4. 2.04%

5. 1.5%   6. 63%

7. 430%   8. 9%

9. 1.46%   10. 2.3%

Answers:
Round 1
1. 0.16   2. 1.12   3. 0.07   4. 0.0204   5. 0.015
6. 0.63   7. 4.3   8. 0.09   9. 0.0146   10. 0.023

Round 2
1. $\frac{4}{25}$ 2. $\frac{28}{25}$ 3. $\frac{7}{100}$ 4. $\frac{51}{2,500}$ 5. $\frac{3}{200}$
6. $\frac{63}{100}$ 7. $\frac{43}{10}$ 8. $\frac{9}{100}$ 9. $\frac{73}{5,000}$ 10. $\frac{23}{1,000}$

Cooperative Learning and Pre-Algebra: Becky Bride
Kagan Publishing • 1 (800) 933-2667 • www.KaganOnline.com

4 APPLICATIONS

Structure: Sage-N-Scribe

Solve each problem.

1. There are 12 girls in a class of 22 students.
   a) What percent of the students are girls?
   b) What percent of the students are boys?

2. A fruit mixture contains 15 percent blueberries. If there are 20 cups of the fruit mix, how many cups of blueberries are there?

3. Wheels R Us sells cars and trucks. If 40 percent of the vehicles on the sales lot are trucks and there are 25 trucks, how many cars are on the sales lot? Round to the nearest whole number.

4. At a pet store, there are 15 puppies and 12 kittens. What percent of the animals are kittens? Round to the nearest hundredths place.

5. A manufacturer determines that 2 percent of the products produced are defective. If 32 products were found defective, how many were initially manufactured?

ACTIVITY 4
APPLICATIONS

Structure: Sage-N-Scribe

6. A tire warranty states that the tire tread should be good for 40,000 miles. If Jill has driven 18,000 miles, what percent of the tire tread remains?

7. A local park ranger estimated there were 62 squirrels, 16 raccoons, 23 opossums, and 27 armadillos in his park. What percent of the park animals are not squirrels? What percent of the animals are opossums and armadillos? Round your answers to the nearest hundredths place.

8. A local middle school had 632 students at the beginning of the year. If 42 students moved away during the school year, what percent of the students stayed enrolled in the school? What percent of the students moved away? Round your answers to the nearest hundredths place.

Answers:

1. a) 55%, b) 45%	2. 3 cups	3. 38 cars	4. 44%
5. 1,600 products	6. 55%	7. 52%, 39%	8. 93%, 7%

Cooperative Learning and Pre-Algebra: Becky Bride
Kagan Publishing • 1 (800) 933-2667 • www.KaganOnline.com

5 FINANCIAL APPLICATIONS

Structure: Sage-N-Scribe

Solve each problem. Round to the hundredths place.

1. Harry sells jewelry and makes a 2 percent commission on his total diamond sales. If he sold $92,000 of diamonds during the month of July, how much money did he make in commission?

2. Amy bought supplies to build a go-cart. If the supplies totaled $189 and the sales tax rate is 7 percent, how much money will she pay in taxes? What is the total cost of the go-cart including tax?

3. A bicycle that normally sells for $520 is on sale with a 30 percent discount. What is the sale price of the bike? What is the total cost of the bike including 5 percent sales tax?

4. The Snyder family's budget includes 8 percent for entertainment. If their monthly income is $3,000, how much money do they have to spend on entertainment each month?

5. Joes earns $4,100 per month and pays $870 each month for rent. What percent of his income is spent on rent?

6. The electric company raised rates 1.5 percent. If Lori's monthly electric bill was $210 a month, how much more money is she spending on electricity? What will her new monthly bill be?

7. Micah bought a stereo system that was on sale. The sale price was $170 and the discount was 30 percent. What was the original price?

8. Nancy earns $7 per hour and 3 percent commission on her total sales. Last pay period, she worked 35 hours and had sales that totaled $27,000. How much money did she earn?

Answers:
1. $1,840   2. $13.23, $202.23   3. $364, $382.20   4. $240
5. 21%   6. $3.15, $213.15   7. $242.86   8. $1,055

ACTIVITY

6 PERCENT INCREASE/DECREASE

Structure: Sage-N-Scribe

Solve each problem. Round to the thousandths place.

1. The price of a movie ticket increased from $7 to $7.80. What was the percent increase in the price of a ticket?

2. The number of students enrolled at Anywhere Middle School went from 832 to 700 students. What was the percent decrease in enrollment?

3. The number of people infected with the flu decreased from 532 people to 305. What was the percent decrease of people infected with the flu?

4. MP3 sales at a local store increased from 106 phones to 200 phones. What is the percent of increase in sales?

5. Alan struck out 18 batters yesterday. Today he only struck out 10. What is the percent of decrease in strike outs?

6. In the first game of paintball, the Eagle team hit 27 targets. In the next game, they hit 35 targets. What is the percent of increase in hits?

7. The eighth grade class sold 1,620 candy bars last year during a fundraiser. This year they sold 1,800. What was the percent of increase in number of candy bars sold?

8. The number of students that attended a volleyball game last week was 75. This week 61 students attended a game. What is the percent of decrease in attendance?

Answers:
1. 11.4%   2. 15.9%   3. 42.7%   4. 88.7%
5. 44.4%   6. 29.6%   7. 11.1%   8. 18.7%

Cooperative Learning and Pre-Algebra: Becky Bride
Kagan Publishing • 1 (800) 933-2667 • www.KaganOnline.com

ACTIVITY

7 GEOMETRIC APPLICATIONS

Structure: Sage-N-Scribe

Solve each problem. Round to the thousandths place. Use 3.14 for π.

1. Beth has a rectangular garden whose dimensions are 12 feet by 4 feet. If bunnies ate 15 percent of the vegetables, how many square feet of garden was not eaten?

2. Tom is making an abstract painting that is 12 inches by 18 inches, with a triangle in the center. If the base of the triangle measures 3 inches and the height is 5 inches, what percent of the painting is covered with the triangle? Round your answer to the nearest tenth.

3. Farmer Stacy has a rectangular field that measures 400 feet by 300 feet. She planted beans in a rectangular region 13 feet by 75 feet, wheat in a rectangular region 15 feet by 100 feet, and the remainder in corn. What percent of the field is corn? Round your answer to the nearest tenth.

4. The side of a rectangular building, which is 60 feet long and 120 feet tall, needs to be painted. It has ten windows that measure 12 feet by 9 feet. What percent will be painted?

GEOMETRIC APPLICATIONS

Structure: Sage-N-Scribe

5. Mark and Guy are shingling a roof. They shingled a rectangular region 20 feet by 40 feet yesterday and 35 feet by 42 feet today. What is the percent increase in the amount shingled today? Round your answer to the nearest thenths place.

6. A circular oil spill grew from a diameter of 10 feet to 75 feet. What is the percent increase in the diameter?

7. A cylindrical bucket has a radius five inches and a height of fourteen inches. If the height of the water in the bucket is six inches, what percent of the bucket is empty?

8. A dog run is rectangular and has dimensions four feet by eight feet. Maria wants to increase the perimeter 40 percent. What will the new perimeter be?

Answers:
1. 40.8 ft²	2. 3.5%	3. 97.9%	4. 85%
5. 83.8%	6. 650%	7. 57.1%	8. 33.6 ft

Cooperative Learning and Pre-Algebra: Becky Bride
Kagan Publishing • 1 (800) 933-2667 • www.KaganOnline.com

ACTIVITY

8 ALL MIXED UP

Structure: Sage-N-Scribe

Solve each problem. Round to the hundredths place.

For problems 1–4, use the following information.
Music R Us sells CD's and DVD's. All of its CD's sell for $15.99 and its DVD's sell for $19.99. The sales tax rate in this community is six percent.

1. Andrew bought two CD's and one DVD. What was the total cost of his purchase?

2. Total sales in January were $24,000 and total sales in February were $40,000. What was the percent increase in sales?

3. During the month of May, the company sold a total of 1,236 items. If 810 were CD's, what percent of the items sold were DVD's?

4. The store is in the shape of a rectangle whose dimensions are 50 feet by 70 feet. If 15 feet by 20 feet are tiled, what percent of the store has carpeting?

5. Thirty-five percent of Anokhee's lawn died. If her yard measures 40 feet by 90 feet, and sod costs $1.50 per square foot, what is the cost to replace the lawn that died?

ACTIVITY

8 ALL MIXED UP

Structure: Sage-N-Scribe

6. Sameerah sells houses. Last month she made $16,975 in commission. If her commission rate is 3.5 percent, what was the value of her total sales?

7. Swathi is renting an apartment for $850 per month. She received a notice from her landlord that her rent will increase 8 percent next year. How much more money will she spend each month in rent? What is her rent for the new year?

8. The Lazy River overflowed its banks and flooded 312 homes. If the community has 2,813 homes, what percentage of the homes were not flooded?

9. Because of high gasoline prices, airlines had to increase fares. The cost to fly has become so expensive that the Fly With Us airline has reduced the number of its daily flights from 325 to 170. Find the percent of decrease in the number of flights.

10. In August, Allison was buying clothes to wear to school. She bought a pair of jeans that were marked down 60 percent. The sales price was $16.99. What was the original price of the jeans?

Answers:
1. $55.09	2. 67%	3. 34%	4. 91%	5. $1,890
6. $485,000	7. $68, $918	8. 89%	9. 48%	10. $42.48

Cooperative Learning and Pre-Algebra: Becky Bride
Kagan Publishing • 1 (800) 933-2667 • www.KaganOnline.com

COORDINATE PLANE

   This chapter builds on the coordinate plane concepts that have been woven throughout Chapters 1–4. Students should already know how to plot points and adjust axes. This chapter reinforces those skills and has students generate tables to graph functions, then has the students graph the ordered pairs contained in the tables.

LESSON

1 GRAPHING

ACTIVITY 1:   Name My Quadrant or Axis
ACTIVITY 2:   Find My Other Coordinates
ACTIVITY 3:   Am I a Solution?
ACTIVITY 4:   Make a Table
ACTIVITY 5:   Graph My Table
ACTIVITY 6:   Graph Me
ACTIVITY 7:   What Did We Learn?

LESSON 1
GRAPHING

This chapter is small because the students have worked with plotting points in the first four chapters and have graphed the same point on several different coordinate planes whose axes had different scales. In Chapter 2 students were introduced to the four quadrants and graphed points in all four quadrants in two subsequent chapters. This lesson begins with a review of these concepts and then has students determine if an ordered pair is a solution to an equation. Students will make tables of x and y values for a given equation. The next lesson requires students to graph the tables that they made. Activity 6 requires students to make a table and graph, combining Activities 4 and 5 into one problem. The lesson ends with a synthesis activity.

1 NAME MY QUADRANT OR AXIS

▶ **Structure**
• RallyCoach

▶ **Materials**
• Transparency 6.1.1
• 1 sheet of graph paper and pencil per pair of students

Graphic

1. Teacher poses many problems using Transparency 6.1.1.

2. Partner A plots the point and names the quadrant or axis the point lies in for problem one, writing his/her response on the paper.

3. Partner B watches, listens, checks, and praises.

4. Partner B plots the point and names the quadrant or axis the point lies in for the next problem, writing his/her response on the paper.

5. Partner A watches, listens, checks, and praises.

6. Repeat for remaining problems starting at step 2.

Cooperative Learning and Pre-Algebra: Becky Bride
Kagan Publishing • 1 (800) 933-2667 • www.KaganOnline.com

ACTIVITY

2 FIND MY OTHER COORDINATES

Graphic

1. Teacher poses many problems using Blackline 6.1.2.

2. Partner A plots the point(s) and names the coordinates that complete the reflection or geometric figure in problem one, writing his/her response on the paper.

3. Partner B watches, listens, checks, and praises.

4. Partner B plots the point(s) and names the coordinates that complete the reflection or geometric figure in the next problem, writing his/her response on the paper.

5. Partner A watches, listens, checks, and praises.

6. Repeat for remaining problems starting at step 2.

▶ **Structure**
• RallyCoach

▶ **Materials**
• Blackline 6.1.2
• 1 sheet of graph paper and pencil per pair of students

ACTIVITY

3 AM I A SOLUTION?

Algebraic

1. Teacher poses many problems using Transparency 6.1.3.

2. Partner A determines if the coordinates in problem one are a solution to the given function, writing his/her response on the paper.

3. Partner B watches, listens, checks, and praises.

4. Partner B determines if the coordinates in the next problem are a solution to the given function, writing his/her response on the paper.

5. Partner A watches, listens, checks, and praises.

6. Repeat for remaining problems starting at step 2.

▶ **Structure**
• RallyCoach

▶ **Materials**
• Transparency 6.1.3
• 1 sheet of paper and pencil per pair of students

ACTIVITY

4

MAKE A TABLE

▶ **Structure**
· Sage-N-Scribe

▶ **Materials**
· Transparency 6.1.4
· 1 sheet of paper and pencil per pair of students

Algebraic

Setup:
In pairs, Student A is the Sage; Student B is the Scribe. Students fold a sheet of paper in half and each writes his/her name on one half.

1. The Sage gives the Scribe step-by-step instructions on how to make a table of solutions for the function in problem one.

2. The Scribe records the Sage's solution step-by-step in writing on the Sage's side of the paper.

3. If the Sage is correct, the Scribe praises the Sage. Otherwise, the Scribe coaches, then praises.

4. Students switch roles for the next problem.

ACTIVITY

5

GRAPH MY TABLE

▶ **Structure**
· Sage-N-Scribe

▶ **Materials**
· Transparencies 6.1.4 and 6.1.4a
· 1 sheet of graph paper and pencil per pair of students

Graphic

Setup:
In pairs, Student A is the Sage; Student B is the Scribe. Students fold a sheet of paper in half and each writes his/her name on one half.

1. The Sage gives the Scribe step-by-step instructions on how to graph the table of values in problem one.

2. The Scribe records the Sage's solution step-by-step in writing on the Sage's side of the paper.

3. If the Sage is correct, the Scribe praises the Sage. Otherwise, the Scribe coaches, then praises.

4. Students switch roles for the next problem.

Cooperative Learning and Pre-Algebra: Becky Bride
Kagan Publishing • 1 (800) 933-2667 • www.KaganOnline.com

ACTIVITY

6 GRAPH ME

Graphic
Algebraic

Setup:
In pairs, Student A is the Sage; Student B is the Scribe. Students fold a sheet of paper in half and each writes his/her name on one half.

1. The Sage gives the Scribe step-by-step instructions on how to make a function table and graph the function in problem one.

2. The Scribe records the Sage's solution step-by-step in writing on the Sage's side of the paper.

3. If the Sage is correct, the Scribe praises the Sage. Otherwise, the Scribe coaches, then praises.

4. Students switch roles for the next problem.

▶ **Structure**
· Sage-N-Scribe

▶ **Materials**
· Transparencies 6.1.5 and 6.1.5a
· 1 sheet of graph paper and pencil per pair of students

ACTIVITY

7 WHAT DID WE LEARN?

Synthesis

1. Each teammate signs his/her name in the upper right corner of the team paper with the colored pen/pencil he/she is using.

2. One teammate writes "*Coordinate Planes*" in the center of the team paper in a rectangle.

3. Teammate 1 shares with the team one core concept he/she learned in the entire unit.

4. The student checks for consensus.

5. The teammates show agreement or lack of agreement with thumbs up or down.

6. If there is agreement, the students celebrate and the teammate records the core concept on the graphic organizer, connecting it with a line to the main idea, *Coordinate Planes*. If not, teammates discuss the response until there is agreement and then they celebrate.

7. Play continues with the next student's core concept, until all core concepts are exhausted.

8. Repeat steps 3–7 with teammates adding details to each core concept and making bridges between related ideas.

▶ **Structure**
· RoundTable Consensus

▶ **Materials**
· 1 large sheet of paper per team
· 1 different color pen or pencil for each student in the team

ACTIVITY

1 **NAME MY QUADRANT OR AXIS**

Structure: RallyCoach

a) Plot the point.
b) Name the quadrant or axis the point lies in.
c) For the points on an axis, identify whether they are *x* or *y*-intercepts.

1. (–5, 2)

2. (–8, –2)

3. (0, 7)

4. (9, –2)

5. (5, 3)

6. (6, 0)

7. (2, –7)

8. (0, –8)

9. (–10, –4)

10. (–6, 8)

Answers:

1. quad II	2. quad III	3. *y*-axis; *y*-intercept	4. quad IV	5. quad I
6. *x*-axis; *x*-intercept	7. quad IV	8. *y*-axis; *y*-intercept	9. quad III	10. quad II

Cooperative Learning and Pre-Algebra: Becky Bride
Kagan Publishing • 1 (800) 933-2667 • www.KaganOnline.com

ACTIVITY

2 FIND MY OTHER COORDINATES

Structure: RallyCoach

Give the coordinates of the point(s) that complete the reflection or geometric figure.

1. Reflection of the point $(-5, -2)$ over the *y*-axis

2. Reflection of the point $(3, -2)$ over the *x*-axis

3. Reflection of the point $(-1, 5)$ over the origin

4. Reflection of the point $(-8, 1)$ over the *y*-axis

5. The point that completes a rectangle if $(-7, 6)$, $(1, 6)$, and $(-7, 3)$ are three vertices

6. The point that completes a trapezoid if $(5, -4)$, $(8, 0)$, and $(1, -4)$ are three vertices

7. The point that completes an isosceles triangle if $(-2, 0)$ and $(-7, -5)$ are two vertices

8. The point that completes a parallelogram if $(-2, 2)$, $(1, 7)$, and $(-1, -2)$ are three vertices

Answers:

1. $(5, -2)$	2. $(3, 2)$	3. $(1, -5)$	4. $(8, 1)$
5. $(1, 3)$	6. $(-2, 0)$	7. $(-7, 5)$, $(-12, 0)$, $(3, -5)$, or $(-2, -10)$	8. $(2, 3)$ or $(0, 11)$

ACTIVITY

3 **AM I A SOLUTION?**

Structure: RallyCoach

For problems 1–4, use the function $2x - 3y = 12$. Determine if the ordered pair is a solution.

1. $(-3, -6)$ 2. $(3, -2)$

3. $(8, 2)$ 4. $(5, -1)$

For problems 5–8, use the function $x^2 - 2y = 48$. Determine if the ordered pair is a solution.

5. $(2, -22)$ 6. $(8, -5)$

7. $(6, -6)$ 8. $(-4, -16)$

Answers:

1. yes	2. yes	3. no	4. no
5. yes	6. no	7. yes	8. yes

Cooperative Learning and Pre-Algebra: Becky Bride
Kagan Publishing • 1 (800) 933-2667 • www.KaganOnline.com

4&5 MAKE A TABLE
GRAPH MY TABLE

Structure: Sage-N-Scribe

Directions:

Activity 4: Make a table of values that are a solution to the given function.

Activity 5: Graph each table from Activity 4 on a different coordinate plane.

1. $2x - 5y = 10$

2. $\dfrac{1}{2}x + 3 = y$

3. $y = \dfrac{2}{3}x - 4$

4. $3x + y = 5$

5. $y = x^2 - 5$

6. $2x^2 - y = 6$

7. $x^2 + 2y = 8$

8. $y = 1 - \dfrac{1}{2}x^2$

Activity 4: Answers will vary.

ACTIVITIES 4&5 MAKE A TABLE GRAPH MY TABLE

Structure: Sage-N-Scribe

Activity 5 Answers:

1.

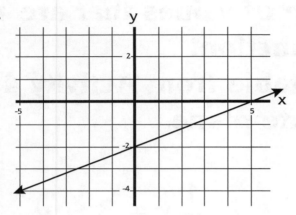

2.

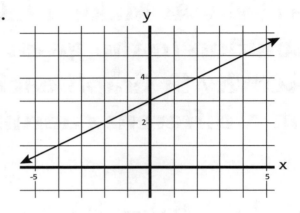

3.

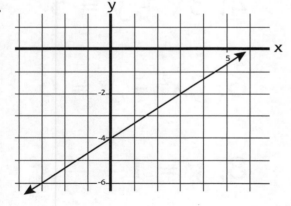

4.

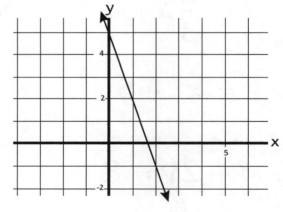

Cooperative Learning and Pre-Algebra: Becky Bride
Kagan Publishing • 1 (800) 933-2667 • www.KaganOnline.com

ACTIVITIES
4&5
MAKE A TABLE
GRAPH MY TABLE

Structure: Sage-N-Scribe

Activity 5 Answers:

5.

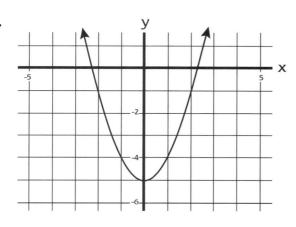

6.

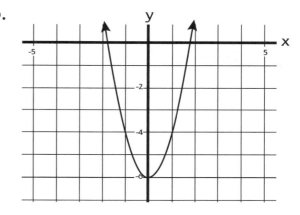

7.

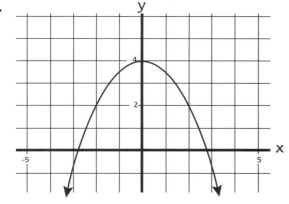

8.

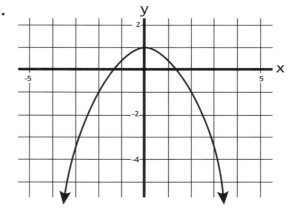

ACTIVITY

6 **GRAPH ME**

Structure: Sage-N-Scribe

Graph each function below on a different coordinate plane by using a table.

1. $x^2 - x = y$

2. $2x + 1 = y$

3. $x + 4y = 8$

4. $x^2 - 4x = y$

5. $y - x = (-5)$

6. $-x - y = 2$

Cooperative Learning and Pre-Algebra: Becky Bride
Kagan Publishing • 1 (800) 933-2667 • www.KaganOnline.com

GRAPH ME

Structure: Sage-N-Scribe

Answers:

1.
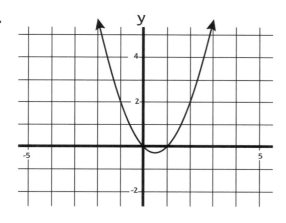

2.
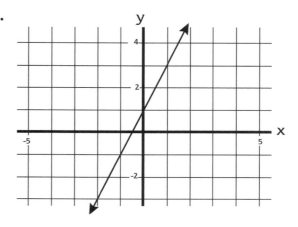

3.
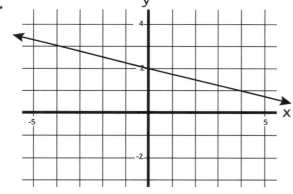

4.
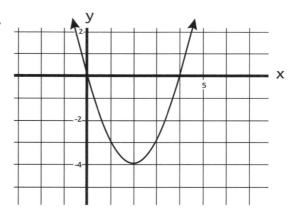

5.
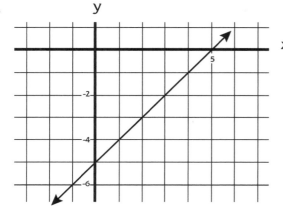

6.
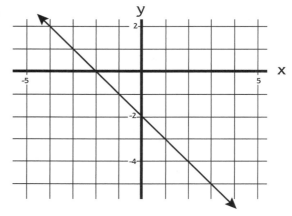

DATA ANALYSIS AND PROBABILITY

This chapter has students work with measures of central tendency and range. Students will also analyze data to determine which measure of central tendency is the best. Lesson 2 has students display data through different graphs. Lesson 3 has students work with sample space, probability, and the counting principle.

LESSON 1 DATA ANALYSIS

ACTIVITY 1: Find My Mean
ACTIVITY 2: Find My Median
ACTIVITY 3: Find My Mode
ACTIVITY 4: Find My Range
ACTIVITY 5: Analyze My Data
ACTIVITY 6: Which Is the Best Measure?
ACTIVITY 7: What Did We Learn?

LESSON 2 STATISTICAL GRAPHS

ACTIVITY 1: Draw a Bar Chart
ACTIVITY 2: Make a Box Plot
ACTIVITY 3: Graph a Scatter Plot
ACTIVITY 4: Construct a Stem Leaf Plot
ACTIVITY 5: Interpret My Stem Leaf Plot
ACTIVITY 6: Interpret My Circle Graph
ACTIVITY 7: What Did We Learn?

LESSON 3 PROBABILITY

ACTIVITY 1: What is the Sample Space?
ACTIVITY 2: Probability and One Number Cube
ACTIVITY 3: Probability and Two Number Cubes
ACTIVITY 4: Probability and Marbles
ACTIVITY 5: Find the Geometric Probability
ACTIVITY 6: How Many Ways?
ACTIVITY 7: What Did We Learn?

LESSON 1
DATA ANALYSIS

This lesson has students work with measures of central tendency: mean, median, and mode. Students will also find the range of data. In the first four activities, the data is in the form of lists. Activity 5 has the data in frequency tables. Activity 6 has students determine which measure of central tendency is the best and asks the students to explain their reasoning. This helps show students that when a list of data has a really high or really low number, the mean can be skewed.

1 FIND MY MEAN

▶ **Structure**
• Sage-N-Scribe

▶ **Materials**
• Blackline 7.1.1 per pair of students
• 1 sheet of paper and pencil per pair of students

Numeric

Setup:
In pairs, Student A is the Sage; Student B is the Scribe. Students fold a sheet of paper in half and each writes his/her name on one half.

1. The Sage gives the Scribe step-by-step instructions on how to find the mean in problem one.

2. The Scribe records the Sage's solution step-by-step in writing on the Sage's side of the paper.

3. If the Sage is correct, the Scribe praises the Sage. Otherwise, the Scribe coaches, then praises.

4. Students switch roles for the next problem.

2 FIND MY MEDIAN

▶ **Structure**
• Sage-N-Scribe

▶ **Materials**
• Blackline 7.1.1 per pair of students
• 1 sheet of paper and pencil per pair of students

Numeric

Setup:
In pairs, Student A is the Sage; Student B is the Scribe. Students fold a sheet of paper in half and each writes his/her name on one half.

1. The Sage gives the Scribe step-by-step instructions on how to find the median in problem one.

2. The Scribe records the Sage's solution step-by-step in writing on the Sage's side of the paper.

3. If the Sage is correct, the Scribe praises the Sage. Otherwise, the Scribe coaches, then praises.

4. Students switch roles for the next problem.

Cooperative Learning and Pre-Algebra: Becky Bride
Kagan Publishing • 1 (800) 933-2667 • www.KaganOnline.com

ACTIVITY
3 FIND MY MODE

Numeric

Setup:
In pairs, Student A is the Sage; Student B is the Scribe. Students fold a sheet of paper in half and each writes his/her name on one half.

1. The Sage gives the Scribe step-by-step instructions on how to find the mode in problem one.

2. The Scribe records the Sage's solution step-by-step in writing on the Sage's side of the paper.

3. If the Sage is correct, the Scribe praises the Sage. Otherwise, the Scribe coaches, then praises.

4. Students switch roles for the next problem.

▶ **Structure**
• Sage-N-Scribe

▶ **Materials**
• Blackline 7.1.1 per pair of students
• 1 sheet of paper and pencil per pair of students

ACTIVITY
4 FIND MY RANGE

Numeric

Setup:
In pairs, Student A is the Sage; Student B is the Scribe. Students fold a sheet of paper in half and each writes his/her name on one half.

1. The Sage gives the Scribe step-by-step instructions on how to find the range in problem one.

2. The Scribe records the Sage's solution step-by-step in writing on the Sage's side of the paper.

3. If the Sage is correct, the Scribe praises the Sage. Otherwise, the Scribe coaches, then praises.

4. Students switch roles for the next problem.

▶ **Structure**
• Sage-N-Scribe

▶ **Materials**
• Blackline 7.1.1 per pair of students
• 1 sheet of paper and pencil per pair of students

ANALYZE MY DATA

▶ **Structure**
- RallyCoach

▶ **Materials**
- Blackline 7.1.2 per pair of students
- 1 sheet of paper and pencil per pair of students

Numeric

1. Teacher poses many problems using Blackline 7.1.2.

2. Partner A writes the data in a list and then finds the mean, median, mode, and range of the data in problem one, writing his/her response on the paper.

3. Partner B watches, listens, checks, and praises.

4. Partner B writes the data in a list and then finds the mean, median, mode, and range of the data for the next problems, writing his/her response on the paper.

5. Partner A watches, listens, checks, and praises.

6. Repeat for remaining problems starting at step 2.

WHICH IS THE BEST MEASURE?

▶ **Structure**
- Sage-N-Scribe

▶ **Materials**
- Blackline 7.1.3 per pair of students
- 1 sheet of paper and pencil per pair of students

Numeric

Setup:
In pairs, Student A is the Sage; Student B is the Scribe. Students fold a sheet of paper in half and each writes his/her name on one half.

1. The Sage gives the Scribe step-by-step instructions on how to find the mean, median, and mode in problem one and then determines which is the best measure of central tendency.

2. The Scribe records the Sage's solution step-by-step in writing on the Sage's side of the paper.

3. If the Sage is correct, the Scribe praises the Sage. Otherwise, the Scribe coaches, then praises.

4. Students switch roles for the next problem.

Cooperative Learning and Pre-Algebra: Becky Bride
Kagan Publishing • 1 (800) 933-2667 • www.KaganOnline.com

WHAT DID WE LEARN?

Synthesis

1. Each teammate signs his/her name in the upper right corner of the team paper with the colored pen/pencil he/she is using.

2. One teammate writes "*Data Analysis*" in the center of the team paper in a rectangle.

3. Teammate 1 shares with the team one core concept he/she learned in the unit.

4. The student checks for consensus.

5. The teammates show agreement or lack of agreement with thumbs up or down.

6. If there is agreement, the students celebrate and the teammate records the core concept on the graphic organizer, connecting it with a line to the main idea, *Data Analysis*. If not, teammates discuss the response until there is agreement and then they celebrate.

7. Play continues with the next student's core concept, until all core concepts are exhausted.

8. Repeat steps 3–7 with teammates adding details to each core concept and making bridges between related ideas.

▶ **Structure**
• RoundTable Consensus

▶ **Materials**
• 1 large sheet of paper per team
• 1 different colored pen or pencil for each student in the team

Chapter 7: Data Analysis and Probability

Lesson One

Blackline 7.1.1

1, 2, 3 & 4 FIND MY MEAN
FIND MY MEDIAN
FIND MY MODE
FIND MY RANGE

Structure: Sage-N-Scribe

Directions:

Activity 1: Find the mean of each set of data. Round answers
to the hundredths place.

Activity 2: Find the median of each set of data. Round answers
to the tenths place.

Activity 3: Find the mode of each set of data.

Activity 4: Find the range of each set of data.

1. 19, 15, 7, 15, 12

2. 20, 11, 8, 14, 17, 20, 20

3. 47, 52, 39, 40, 55, 52, 41, 40, 52, 60

4. 61, 41, 48, 53, 61, 58, 50, 61, 44, 40, 61, 48

5. 74, 95, 83, 70, 76, 88, 95, 76

6. 100, 81, 75, 87, 81, 93, 75, 99, 75, 94

Answers:

Activity 1

1. 13.6	2. 15.71	3. 47.8	4. 52.17	5. 82.13	6. 86

Activity 2

1. 15	2. 17	3. 49.5	4. 51.5	5. 79.5	6. 84

Activity 3

1. 15	2. 20	3. 52	4. 61	5. 95 & 76	6. 75

Activity 4

1. 12	2. 12	3. 21	4. 21	5. 25	6. 25

Cooperative Learning and Pre-Algebra: Becky Bride
Kagan Publishing • 1 (800) 933-2667 • www.KaganOnline.com

5 ANALYZE MY DATA

Structure: RallyCoach

1. Quiz Grades on a Ten-Point Quiz

Score	10	9	8	7	6
Frequency	3	7	6	4	2

a. Write the data as a list.

b. Find the mean.

c. Find the median.

d. Find the mode.

e. Find the range.

2. Hourly Wage of Employees

Wage	$20	$17.50	$15.00	$10.00	$6.50
Frequency	1	1	3	4	6

a. Write the data as a list.

b. Find the median.

c. Find the mean.

d. Find the range.

e. Find the mode.

ACTIVITY
5 **ANALYZE MY DATA**

Structure: RallyCoach

3. Employee Car Sales

Sales (in thousands)	43	58	60	74	112	150	133
Frequency	2	3	3	5	4	8	6

a. Write the data as a list.

b. Find the mode.

c. Find the range.

d. Find the median.

e. Find the mean.

4. Increase in the Cost of a Barrel of Oil (Month of April)

Price Increase	$1.00	$1.50	$2.00	$2.50	$3.00	$3.50	$4.00
Frequency	8	1	4	9	3	3	2

a. Write the data as a list.

b. Find the median.

c. Find the mean.

d. Find the range.

e. Find the mode.

Answers for Activity 5:
1a. 10, 10, 10, 9, 9, 9, 9, 9, 9, 9, 8, 8, 8, 8, 8, 8, 7, 7, 7, 7, 6, 6
  b. 8.23   c. 8   d. 9   e. 4

2a. 20, 17.50, 15, 15, 15, 10, 10, 10, 10, 6.5, 6.5, 6.5, 6.5, 6.5, 6.5
  b. 10   c. 10.77   d. 13.5   e. 6.5

3a. 43, 43, 58, 58, 58, 60, 60, 60, 74, 74, 74, 74, 74, 112, 112, 112, 112, 150, 150, 150, 150, 150, 150,
    150, 150, 133, 133, 133, 133, 133, 133
  b. 150   c. 90   d. 112   e. 105.03

4a. 1, 1, 1, 1, 1, 1, 1, 1, 1.5, 2, 2, 2, 2, 2.5, 2.5, 2.5, 2.5, 2.5, 2.5, 2.5, 2.5, 2.5, 3, 3, 3, 3.5, 3.5, 3.5, 4, 4
  b. 2.5   c. 2.25   d. 3   e. 2.5

Cooperative Learning and Pre-Algebra: Becky Bride
Kagan Publishing • 1 (800) 933-2667 • www.KaganOnline.com

6 WHICH IS THE BEST MEASURE?

Structure: Sage-N-Scribe

Find each measure of central tendency, then determine which measure best describes the center of the data. Explain your reasoning.

1. In a very small town of 5 people, the salaries earned were $18,000, $450,000, $18,000, $30,000, and $35,000. Which measure of central tendency best represents the data? Explain.

2. Which measure of central tendency best describes the quiz grades? Explain.

Quiz Scores on a Twenty Point Quiz

Score	20	19	17	16	15
Frequency	3	8	10	2	2

3. Which measure of central tendency best describes the test scores? Explain.

Test Scores

Score	100	92	84	76	60	52	36
Frequency	3	8	5	8	2	1	1

4. Which measure of central tendency best describes the price of homes in the community?

Price of Homes

Price (in thousands)	300	280	250	230	110
Frequency		3	5	15	16	1

Answers:
1. Mean: $110,200, median: $30,000, mode: $18,000
2. Mean: 17.76, median: 17, mode: 17
3. Mean: 81.14, median: 84, mode: 92 and 76
4. Mean: $246,000, median: 250,000, mode: $230,000

LESSON 2:
STATISTICAL GRAPHS

In this lesson, the students will construct several different types of graphs to organize data. Bar Charts, box plots, scatter plots, and stem leaf plots are the graphs students will construct. Students will take a stem leaf plot and extract the data and then analyze the data with skills they learned in Lesson 1. Students will interpret a circle graph in Activity 6. The lesson ends with an activity where the students will synthesize what they have learned.

1 DRAW A BAR CHART

▶ **Structure**
• RallyCoach

▶ **Materials**
• Blackline 7.2.1 per pair of students
• Transparency 7.2.1a
• 1 sheet of paper and pencil per pair of students

Graphic

1. Teacher poses many problems using Blackline 7.2.1.

2. Partner A draws a histogram for problem one on the paper.

3. Partner B watches, listens, checks, and praises.

4. Partner B draws a bar chart for the next problem on the paper.

5. Partner A watches, listens, checks, and praises.

6. Repeat for remaining problems starting at step 2.

ACTIVITY

2 MAKE A BOX PLOT

▶ **Structure**
• RallyCoach

▶ **Materials**
• Blackline 7.2.2 per pair of students
• Transparency 7.2.2a
• 1 sheet of paper and pencil per pair of students

Graphic

1. Teacher poses many problems using Blackline 7.2.2.

2. Partner A draws a box plot for problem one on the paper.

3. Partner B watches, listens, checks, and praises.

4. Partner B draws a box plot for the next problem on the paper.

5. Partner A watches, listens, checks, and praises.

6. Repeat for remaining problems starting at step 2.

ACTIVITY 3

GRAPH A SCATTER PLOT

Graphic

1. Teacher poses many problems using Blackline 7.2.3.

2. Partner A draws a scatter plot for problem one, writing his/her response on the graph paper.

3. Partner B watches, listens, checks, and praises.

4. Partner B draws a scatter plot for the next problem, writing his/her response on the graph paper.

5. Partner A watches, listens, checks, and praises.

6. Repeat for remaining problems starting at step 2.

▶ **Structure**
• RallyCoach

▶ **Materials**
• Blackline 7.2.3 per pair of students
• Transparency 7.2.3a
• 1 sheet of graph paper and pencil per pair of students

ACTIVITY 4

CONSTRUCT A STEM LEAF PLOT

Graphic

1. Teacher poses many problems using Blackline 7.2.4.

2. Partner A constructs a stem leaf plot for problem one, writing his/her response on the paper.

3. Partner B watches, listens, checks, and praises.

4. Partner B constructs a stem leaf plot for the next problem, writing his/her response on the paper.

5. Partner A watches, listens, checks, and praises.

6. Repeat for remaining problems starting at step 2.

▶ **Structure**
• RallyCoach

▶ **Materials**
• Blackline 7.2.4 per pair of students
• Transparency 7.2.4a
• 1 sheet of paper and pencil per pair of students

ACTIVITY 5

INTERPRET MY STEM LEAF PLOT

Graphic

Setup:
In pairs, Student A is the Sage; Student B is the Scribe. Students fold a sheet of paper in half and each writes his/her name on one half.

1. The Sage gives the Scribe step-by-step instructions on how to do problem one.

2. The Scribe records the Sage's solution step-by-step in writing on the Sage's side of the paper.

3. If the Sage is correct, the Scribe praises the Sage. Otherwise, the Scribe coaches, then praises.

4. Students switch roles for the next problem.

▶ **Structure**
• Sage-N-Scribe

▶ **Mat~~erials~~**
• Blac~~kline~~ stud~~ents~~
• 1 sh~~eet~~ per

Cooperative Learning and Pre-Algebra: Becky Bride
Kagan Publishing • 1 (800) 933-2667 • www.KaganOnline.com

ACTIVITY
6

INTERPRET MY CIRCLE GRAPH

▶ **Structure:**
• Sage-N-Scribe

▶ **Materials**
• Blackline 7.2.6 per pair of students
• 1 sheet of paper and pencil per pair of students

Numeric

Setup:
In pairs, Student A is the Sage; Student B is the Scribe. Students fold a sheet of paper in half and each writes his/her name on one half.

1. The Sage gives the Scribe step-by-step instructions on how to do problem one.

2. The Scribe records the Sage's solution step-by-step in writing on the Sage's side of the paper.

3. If the Sage is correct, the Scribe praises the Sage. Otherwise, the Scribe coaches, then praises.

4. Students switch roles for the next problem.

ACTIVITY
7

WHAT DID WE LEARN?

▶ **Structure**
• RoundTable Consensus

▶ **Material**
• 1 large sheet of paper per team
• 1 different colored pen or pencil for each student in the team

Synthesis

1. Each teammate signs his/her name in the upper right corner of the team paper with the colored pen/pencil he/she is using.

2. One teammate writes "*Graphs*" in the center of the team paper in a rectangle.

3. Teammate 1 shares with the team one core concept he/she learned in the unit.

4. The student checks for consensus.

5. The teammates show agreement or lack of agreement with thumbs up or down.

6. If there is agreement, the students celebrate and the teammate records the core concept on the graphic organizer, connecting it with a line to the main idea, *Graphs*. If not, teammates discuss the response until there is agreement and then they celebrate.

7. Play continues with the next student's core concept, until all core concepts are exhausted.

8. Repeat steps 3–7 with teammates adding details to each core concept and making bridges between related ideas.

1 DRAW A BAR CHART

Structure: RallyCoach

For each problem, draw a bar chart.

1. Costliest U.S. Weather Disasters

Weather Disaster	Cost in Billions
2005 Hurricane Katrina	$133.8
1988 Drought and Heat Wave	$71.2
1980 Drought and Heat Wave	$55.4
1992 Hurricane Andrew	$40
1993 Midwest Floods	$30.2

National Climatic Data Center

2. Deaths Caused by U.S. Weather Disasters

Weather Disaster	Number of Deaths
2005 Hurricane Katrina	1,833
1988 Drought and Heat Wave	7,500
1980 Drought and Heat Wave	10,000
1992 Hurricane Andrew	61
1993 Midwest Floods	48

National Climatic Data Center

ACTIVITY

1 DRAW A BAR CHART

Structure: RallyCoach

3. Bag of M&M®'s

Color	Number of M&M®'s
Red	5
Green	9
Yellow	5
Orange	7
Blue	12
Brown	3

4. Traffic Accidents in March

Cause	Number
Running a Red Light	8
Improper Lane Change	14
Driving Under the Influence	7
Improper Turn	23
Distracted Driver	18
Falling Asleep	5

Cooperative Learning and Pre-Algebra: Becky Bride
Kagan Publishing • 1 (800) 933-2667 • www.KaganOnline.com

1 DRAW A BAR CHART

Structure: RallyCoach

Activity 1 Answers:

1.

Costliest U.S. Weather Disasters

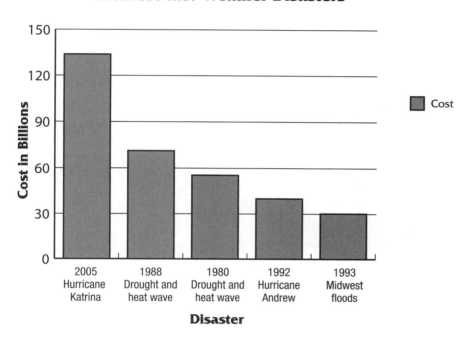

2.

Deaths Caused by U.S. Weather Disasters

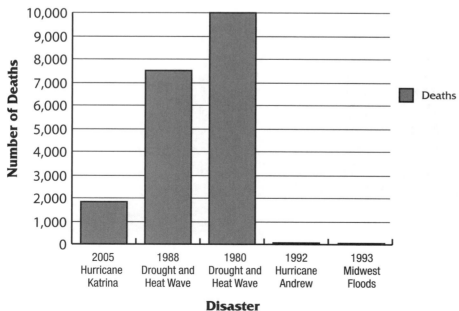

ACTIVITY

1 DRAW A BAR CHART

Structure: RallyCoach

3.

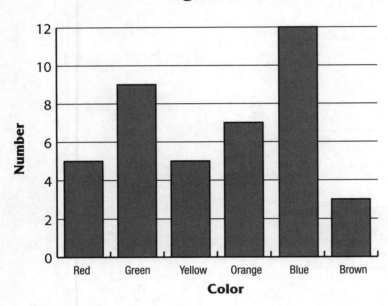

Bag of M&M®'s

4.

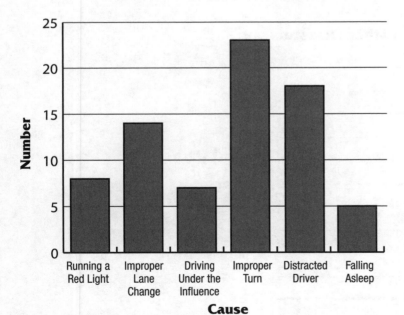

Traffic Accidents in March

Cooperative Learning and Pre-Algebra: Becky Bride
Kagan Publishing • 1 (800) 933-2667 • www.KaganOnline.com

MAKE A BOX PLOT

Structure: RallyCoach

For each of the following, draw a box plot.

1. 9, 16, 12, 12, 8, 25, 19

2. 29, 41, 53, 58, 39, 61, 63, 49

3. 16, 76, 45, 67, 58, 48, 55, 58

4. 71, 19, 25, 33, 25, 15, 13, 4, 12

5. 2.5, 9.8, 6.7, 12.9, 18.3, 30.1, 14.2, 8.7, 13.5, 10.6

6. 27.6, 16.1, 29.3, 31.8, 42.9, 21.3, 16.1, 51.3, 37.2, 41.6

2 MAKE A BOX PLOT

Structure: RallyCoach

Activity 2 Answers:

1.
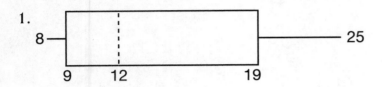

2.
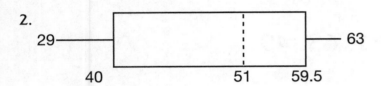

3.
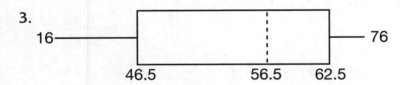

4.
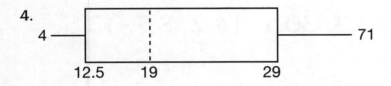

5.
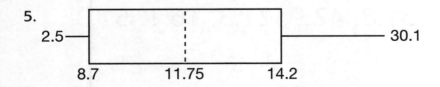

6.
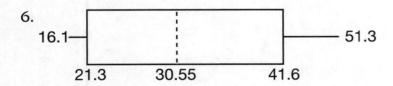

Cooperative Learning and Pre-Algebra: Becky Bride
Kagan Publishing • 1 (800) 933-2667 • www.KaganOnline.com

GRAPH A SCATTER PLOT

Structure: RallyCoach

Make a scatter plot for each problem.

1.
Studying vs. Grade on Test

Hours Studied	0.1	0.4	0.8	1	1.2	1.5	1.8	2
Grade on Test	50	68	72	85	84	96	95	98

2.
Yearly Income

Years of School	6	8	10	12	14	16	18	20
Yearly Income (thousands)	15	16	18	24	30	38	55	120

3.
Gallons of Gas in Gas Tank

Number of Miles Driven	55	90	105	155	190	210	260	300	320	350
Gallons of Gas in Tank	16.4	15.1	14.6	13.2	12.1	11.4	8.9	7.5	6.8	5.9

4.
Bunny Population

Months	2	4	10	16	20	24	30
Bunny Population	2	10	36	64	105	144	200

ACTIVITY

3

GRAPH A SCATTER PLOT

Structure: RallyCoach

Activity 3 Answers:

1.

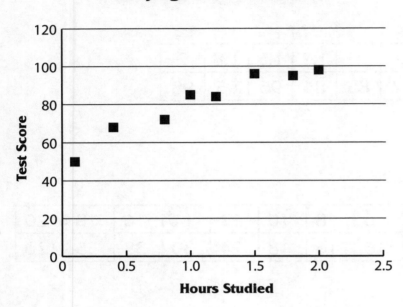

2.

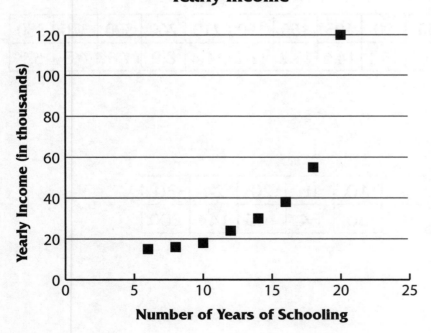

Cooperative Learning and Pre-Algebra: Becky Bride
Kagan Publishing • 1 (800) 933-2667 • www.KaganOnline.com

ACTIVITY

3

GRAPH A SCATTER PLOT

Structure: RallyCoach

3.

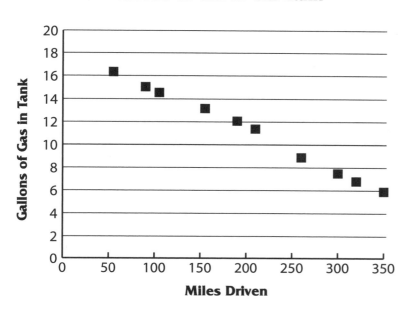

Gallons of Gas in Gas Tank

4.

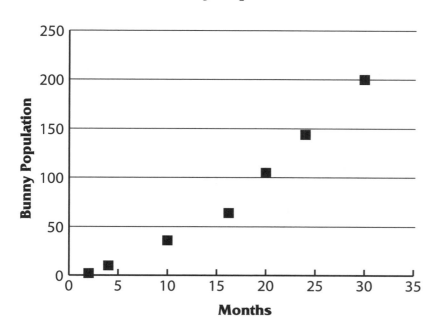

Bunny Population

4 CONSTRUCT A STEM LEAF PLOT

Structure: RallyCoach

For each problem, construct a Stem Leaf Plot.

1. 9, 6, 4, 8, 17, 11, 12, 11, 27, 29, 33

2. 4, 18, 43, 37, 21, 25, 32, 55, 59, 62, 25

3. 63, 59, 83, 57, 71, 62, 67, 85, 76, 71, 101, 109, 115

4. 137, 122, 128, 107, 119, 92, 93, 95, 127, 111, 108

5. 126, 129, 114, 108, 122, 96, 103, 135, 115, 102, 118, 132

6. 610, 614, 633, 658, 654, 621, 642, 627, 635, 649, 633, 639, 621, 619, 661

Cooperative Learning and Pre-Algebra: Becky Bride
Kagan Publishing • 1 (800) 933-2667 • www.KaganOnline.com

ACTIVITY

4 CONSTRUCT A STEM LEAF PLOT

Structure: RallyCoach

Activity 4 Answers:

1.
Stem	Leaves
0	4, 6, 8, 9
1	1, 1, 2, 7
2	7, 9
3	3

2.
Stem	Leaves
0	4
1	8
2	1, 5, 5
3	2, 7
4	3
5	5, 9
6	2

3.
Stem	Leaves
5	7, 9
6	2, 3, 7
7	1, 1, 6
8	3, 5
10	1, 9
11	5

4.
Stem	Leaves
9	2, 3, 5
10	7, 8
11	1, 9
12	2, 7, 8
13	7

5.
Stem	Leaves
9	6
10	2, 3, 8
11	4, 5, 8
12	2, 6, 9
13	2, 5

6.
Stem	Leaves
61	0, 4, 9
62	1, 1, 7
63	3, 3, 5, 9
64	2, 9
65	4, 8
66	1

ACTIVITY

5 INTERPRET MY STEM LEAF PLOT

Structure: Sage-N-Scribe

For problems 1–7, use the graph below. The graph represents the weights of dogs at a local animal shelter. Round to the nearest hundredth.

Stem	Leaves
	6, 7, 7, 9
1	2, 4, 8, 8, 8
2	1, 4, 4, 9
3	3, 5, 5, 7, 8, 9
4	4, 8, 9
5	2, 4
6	5

1. Write the data as a list.

2. Find the mean.

3. Find the median.

4. Find the mode.

5. Find the range.

6. Which is the best measure of central tendency? Explain.

7. What percent of the weights are above 39 pounds?

Cooperative Learning and Pre-Algebra: Becky Bride
Kagan Publishing • 1 (800) 933-2667 • www.KaganOnline.com

ACTIVITY

5 **INTERPRET MY STEM LEAF PLOT**

Structure: Sage-N-Scribe

For problems 8–14, use the graph below. The graph represents the price of cars at a local dealership, in the thousands.

Stem	Leaves
1	2, 4, 5, 5, 5, 8
2	0, 1, 3, 3, 4, 7, 9, 9, 9, 9
3	0, 1, 2, 5, 5, 8, 8, 9
4	2, 5, 6, 6, 7
5	8

8. Write the data as a list.

9. Find the mean. Round to the nearest thousand.

10. Find the median.

11. Find the mode.

12. Find the range.

13. Which is the best measure of central tendency? Explain.

14. What percent of cars are between $25,000 and $36,000? Round to the nearest tenth of a percent.

Answers:
1. 6, 7, 7, 9, 12, 14, 18, 18, 18, 21, 24, 24, 29, 33, 35, 35, 37, 38, 39, 44, 48, 49 52, 54, 65
2. 29.44
3. 29
4. 18
5. 59
6. mean or median because they are so close and there are not any really small or large numbers
7. 24%
8. 12, 14, 15, 15, 15, 18, 20, 21, 23, 23, 24, 27, 29, 29, 29, 29, 30, 31, 32, 35, 35, 38, 38, 39, 42, 45, 46, 46, 47, 58
9. 30,000
10. 29,000
11. 29,000
12. 46,000
13. median or mode because a little more than half the data is 29,000 or below
14. 33.3%

6 INTERPRET MY CIRCLE GRAPH

Structure: Sage-N-Scribe

For problems 1–5 use the circle graph below. The graph represents the budget of a family whose monthly income is $3,200.

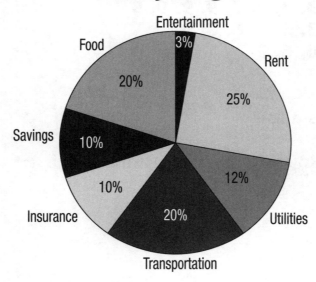

Family Budget

1. How much money does the family pay in rent each month?

2. How much money does the family spend in transportation?

3. How much money does the family spend on utilities?

4. How much money does the family spend each month on entertainment?

5. If the rent increases by 2%, how much more must the family earn each month to pay the increase?

Cooperative Learning and Pre-Algebra: Becky Bride
Kagan Publishing • 1 (800) 933-2667 • www.KaganOnline.com

ACTIVITY

6 INTERPRET MY CIRCLE GRAPH

Structure: Sage-N-Scribe

For problems 6–10, use the circle graph below. The graph represents the percentage of sales by vehicles that Wheels R Us has each month. Round to the nearest whole number.

Wheels R Us Sales

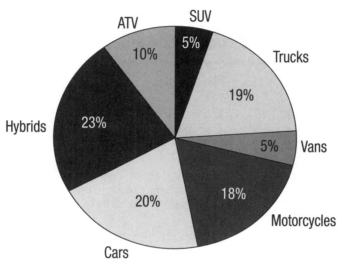

6. In June, the company sold 1,200 vehicles. How many motorcycles were sold?

7. In August, the company sold 1,850 vehicles. How many hybrids or cars were sold?

8. In October, the company sold 210 trucks. How many total vehicles were sold that month?

9. In November, the company sold 40 ATVs. How many trucks did they sell that month?

10. In December, the company sold 82 vans. How many ATVs and motorcycles did they sell?

Answers:

1. $800	2. $640	3. $384	4. $96	5. $16
6. 216	7. 796	8. 1,105	9. 76	10. 459

LESSON 3
PROBABILITY

This lesson begins with students determining sample space. This activity will be important for Activity 3. The next two activities involve probabilities with number cubes. Activity 4 has students compute probability, with or without replacement. Activity 5 reinforces geometric concepts as students find geometric probability. Activity 6 has students work with elementary combinations.

WHAT IS THE SAMPLE SPACE?

▶ **Structure**
· RallyCoach

▶ **Materials**
· Transparency 7.3.1 and Transparency 7.3.1a
· 1 sheet of paper and pencil per pair of students

Numeric

1. Teacher poses many problems using Transparency 7.3.1.

2. Partner A determines the sample space for problem one, writing his/her response on the paper.

3. Partner B watches, listens, checks, and praises.

4. Partner B determines the sample space in the next problem, writing his/her response on the paper.

5. Partner A watches, listens, checks, and praises.

6. Repeat for remaining problems starting at step 2.

PROBABILITY AND ONE NUMBER CUBE

▶ **Structure**
· RallyCoach

▶ **Materials**
· Blackline 7.3.2 per pair of students
· 1 sheet of paper and pencil per pair of students

Numeric

1. Teacher poses many problems using Blackline 7.3.2.

2. Partner A determines the probability for problem one, writing his/her response on the paper.

3. Partner B watches, listens, checks, and praises.

4. Partner B determines the probability for the next problem, writing his/her response on the paper.

5. Partner A watches, listens, checks, and praises.

6. Repeat for remaining problems starting at step 2.

Cooperative Learning and Pre-Algebra: Becky Bride
Kagan Publishing • 1 (800) 933-2667 • www.KaganOnline.com

ACTIVITY 3

PROBABILITY AND TWO NUMBER CUBES

Numeric

1. Teacher poses many problems using Blackline 7.3.3.

2. Partner A determines the probability for problem one, writing his/her response on the paper.

3. Partner B watches, listens, checks, and praises.

4. Partner B determines the probability for the next problem, writing his/her response on the paper.

5. Partner A watches, listens, checks, and praises.

6. Repeat for remaining problems starting at step 2.

▶ **Structure**
• RallyCoach

▶ **Materials**
• Blackline 7.3.3 per pair of students
• 1 sheet of paper and pencil per pair of students

ACTIVITY 4

PROBABILITY AND MARBLES

Numeric

1. Teacher poses many problems using Blackline 7.3.4.

2. Partner A determines the probability for problem one, writing his/her response on the paper.

3. Partner B watches, listens, checks, and praises.

4. Partner B determines the probability for the next problem, writing his/her response on the paper.

5. Partner A watches, listens, checks, and praises.

6. Repeat for remaining problems starting at step 2.

▶ **Structure**
• RallyCoach

▶ **Materials**
• Blackline 7.3.4 per pair of students
• 1 sheet of paper and pencil per pair of students

ACTIVITY 5

FIND THE GEOMETRIC PROBABILITY

Numeric

Setup:
In pairs, Student A is the Sage; Student B is the Scribe. Students fold a sheet of paper in half and each writes his/her name on one half.

1. The Sage gives the Scribe step-by-step instructions on how to find the probability in problem one.

2. The Scribe records the Sage's solution step-by-step in writing on the Sage's side of the paper.

3. If the Sage is correct, the Scribe praises the Sage. Otherwise, the Scribe coaches, then praises.

4. Students switch roles for the next problem.

▶ **Structure**
• Sage-N-Scribe

▶ **Materials**
• Blackline 7.3.5 per pair of students
• 1 sheet of paper and pencil per pair of students

Chapter 7: Data Analysis and Probability   Lesson Three

ACTIVITY

6 HOW MANY WAYS?

▶ **Structure**
• RallyCoach

▶ **Materials**
• Blackline 7.3.6 per pair of students
• 1 sheet of paper and pencil per pair of students

Numeric

1. Teacher poses many problems using Blackline 7.3.6.

2. Partner A does problem one, writing his/her response on the paper.

3. Partner B watches, listens, checks, and praises.

4. Partner B does the next problem, writing his/her response on the paper.

5. Partner A watches, listens, checks, and praises.

6. Repeat for remaining problems starting at step 2.

ACTIVITY

7 WHAT DID WE LEARN?

▶ **Structure**
• RoundTable Consensus

▶ **Materials**
• 1 large sheet of paper per team
• 1 different colored pen or pencil for each student in the team

Synthesis

1. Each teammate signs his/her name in the upper right corner of the team paper with the colored pen/pencil he/she is using.

2. One teammate writes "*Probability*" in the center of the team paper in a rectangle.

3. Teammate 1 shares with the team one core concept he/she learned in the unit.

4. The student checks for consensus.

5. The teammates show agreement or lack of agreement with thumbs up or down.

6. If there is agreement, the students celebrate and the teammate records the core concept on the graphic organizer, connecting it with a line to the main idea, *Probability*. If not, teammates discuss the response until there is agreement and then they celebrate.

7. Play continues with the next student's core concept, until all core concepts are exhausted.

8. Repeat steps 3–7 with teammates adding details to each core concept and making bridges between related ideas.

Cooperative Learning and Pre-Algebra: Becky Bride
Kagan Publishing • 1 (800) 933-2667 • www.KaganOnline.com

WHAT IS THE SAMPLE SPACE?

Structure: RallyCoach

Determine the sample space for each problem below.

1. 1 number cube with 6 sides

2. Combination of 2 number cubes with 6 sides

3. Combination of 2 spinners that each have a red, blue, and yellow sector

4. Number of outfits that can be made with a blue shirt, white shirt, jeans, black pants, and skirt

5. Number of sandwiches that can be made with white bread, wheat bread, ham, turkey, roast beef, and tuna if each sandwich has only 1 type of meat

6. Number pizzas that can be made with deep-dish crust, thin crust, pepperoni, sausage, ham, onion, and mushrooms if each pizza has one topping

1 WHAT IS THE SAMPLE SPACE?

Structure: RallyCoach

Activity 1 Answers:

1. 1, 2, 3, 4, 5, 6

2.

	1	2	3	4	5	6
1	1,1	1,2	1,3	1,4	1,5	1,6
2	2,1	2,2	2,3	2,4	2,5	2,6
3	3,1	3,2	3,3	3,4	3,5	3,6
4	4,1	4,2	4,3	4,4	4,5	4,6
5	5,1	5,2	5,3	5,4	5,5	5,6
6	6,1	6,2	6,3	6,4	6,5	6,6

3. r = red   b = blue   y = yellow

   r,r   r,b   r,y   b,r   b,b   b,y   y,r   y,b   y,y

4. b = blue shirt   w = white shirt   j = jeans
   p = black pants   s = skirt

   b,j   w,j   b,p   w,p   b,s   w,s

5. w = white bread   wh = wheat bread   h = ham
   t = turkey   r = roast beef   f = tuna

   t,w   t,wh   h,w   h,wh   r,w   r,wh   f,w   f,wh

6. d = deep-dish crust   t = thin crust   p = pepperoni
   s = sausage   h = ham   o = onion   m = mushroom

   p,d   p,t   s,d   s,t   h,d   h,t   o,d   o,t   m,d   m,t

Cooperative Learning and Pre-Algebra: Becky Bride
Kagan Publishing • 1 (800) 933-2667 • www.KaganOnline.com

PROBABILITY AND
ONE NUMBER CUBE

Structure: RallyCoach

A number cube with six sides is rolled. Find the requested probability.

1. P(even number)

2. P(number is less than 4)

3. P(number is greater than or equal to 5)

4. P(number is greater than 0)

5. P(2 or 3)

6. P(not 5)

7. P(number greater than 6)

8. P(even number or 5)

9. P(not 1 or 4)

10. P(not an even number or not 1)

Answers:

1. $\frac{1}{2}$ 2. $\frac{1}{2}$ 3. $\frac{1}{3}$ 4. 1   5. $\frac{1}{3}$

6. $\frac{5}{6}$ 7. 0   8. $\frac{2}{3}$ 9. $\frac{2}{3}$ 10. $\frac{1}{3}$

ACTIVITY
3

PROBABILITY AND TWO NUMBER CUBES

Structure: RallyCoach

Two 6-sided number cubes are rolled. Find the probability of each of the following.

1. P(two 5's)

2. P(sum of the numbers is less than 7)

3. P(both cubes are odd)

4. P(1 cube is odd and 1 cube is even)

5. P(both are the same number)

6. P(product of the numbers is 12)

7. P(sum of the numbers is less than 6)

8. P(at least 1 cube is a 2)

Answers:
1. $\frac{1}{36}$ 2. $\frac{15}{36}$ 3. $\frac{1}{4}$ 4. $\frac{1}{2}$

5. $\frac{1}{6}$ 6. $\frac{1}{9}$ 7. $\frac{5}{18}$ 8. $\frac{11}{36}$

Cooperative Learning and Pre-Algebra: Becky Bride
Kagan Publishing • 1 (800) 933-2667 • www.KaganOnline.com

4 PROBABILITY AND MARBLES

Structure: RallyCoach

A bag contains 6 red marbles, 4 purple marbles, and 2 blue marbles.

For problems 1–6 one marble is picked out of the bag. Find the requested probability.

1. P(red)

2. P(purple)

3. P(red or blue)

4. P(not blue)

5. P(not purple)

6. P(purple or blue)

For problems 7–12, one marble is chosen, then another one is chosen. Find the requested probability.

7. P (red then blue) with replacement

8. P(blue then blue) with replacement

9. P(purple then purple) without replacement

10. P(purple then blue) without replacement

11. P(red then red then blue) with replacement

12. P(purple then red then blue) without replacement

Answers:

1. $\frac{1}{2}$ 2. $\frac{1}{3}$ 3. $\frac{2}{3}$ 4. $\frac{5}{6}$ 5. $\frac{2}{3}$ 6. $\frac{1}{2}$

7. $\frac{1}{12}$ 8. $\frac{1}{36}$ 9. $\frac{1}{11}$ 10. $\frac{2}{33}$ 11. $\frac{1}{24}$ 12. $\frac{2}{55}$

ACTIVITY
5

FIND THE GEOMETRIC PROBABILITY

Structure: Sage-N-Scribe

Write all answers as percents.

For problems 1–2 a rectangle whose dimensions are 4 inches by 3 inches is inside a circle whose diameter is 6 inches. If a pebble is dropped onto the circle, find the following probabilities. Use 3.14 for π.

1. P(pebble lands inside the rectangle). Round to the hundredths place.

2. P(pebble lands outside the rectangle but inside the circle).

For problems 3–10, use the diagram below. The target has 4 concentric circles. The radius of the center circle is 1 inch, the radius of the next circle is 3 inches, the radius of the third circle from the center is 6 inches, and the radius of the outer circle is 10 inches. These circles are mounted on a square board whose sides are 24 inches. If a dart is thrown, find the following probabilities. Use 3.14 for π.

3. P(bull's-eye) round to the thousandths place

4. P(dart falls in ring c)

5. P(dart falls in ring d)

6. P(dart falls in ring b)

7. P(dart falls outside all circles)

8. P(dart falls in bull's-eye or ring b)

9. P(dart is not in ring c)

10. P(dart is not in ring d)

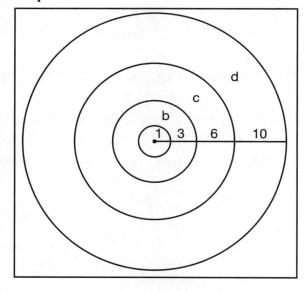

Answers:

1. 42%	2. 58%	3. 0.5%	4. 15%	5. 35%
6. 4%	7. 45%	8. 5%	9. 85%	10. 65%

Cooperative Learning and Pre-Algebra: Becky Bride
Kagan Publishing • 1 (800) 933-2667 • www.KaganOnline.com

6 HOW MANY WAYS?

Structure: RallyCoach

1. How many different outfits can Danny make with 4 shirts, 3 pairs of pants, 2 ties, and 2 pairs of shoes?

2. How many different sandwiches can be made with 3 different meats, 3 different breads, and 4 different cheeses if each sandwich has 1 type of bread, meat, and cheese?

For problems 3–4, a pizza shop has 3 different crusts, 4 different meats, and 4 different vegetables to make pizzas.

3. How many different pizzas can be made with 2 meats and 2 vegetables if no meats and vegetables can be repeated?

4. How many different pizzas can be made with 1 meat and 3 vegetables if no ingredients can be repeated?

5. How many license plates containing three letters and three numbers can be made if letters and numbers cannot repeat?

6. How many license plates containing three letters and three numbers can be made if the first letter must be a vowel, the second letter must be a consonant, and numbers and letters can be repeated?

7. How many different cars can be made with 4 different models, 6 different exterior colors, and 3 different interior colors?

8. How many ways can 10 fiction books, 3 biographies, and 5 nonfiction books be arranged on a shelf?

Answers:
1. 48   2. 36   3. 432   4. 288
5. 11,232,000 6. 2,730,000   7. 72   8. 150

NOTES

NOTES

NOTES